1969

GRIM
Fairy Tales
for Adults

"We should be thankful we cannot see the horrors and degradations lying around our childhood, in cupboards and bookshelves, everywhere."

—GRAHAM GREENE,
The Power and the Glory

GRIM
Fairy Tales for Adults

By JOEL WELLS

Illustrated by Marilyn Fitschen

The Macmillan Company, New York

Collier-Macmillan Ltd., London

For Elizabeth, Edith and William Wells

*The author wishes to express his thanks
for the various manners and degrees of
help and encouragement he has received
from Dan Herr, Betty Bartelme and Tom
Brennan—all of whom are now perfectly
free to regret it to a proportionate extent.*

Library of Congress Catalog Card Number: 67-19683
FIRST PRINTING

DISCLAIMER

All of the material in this book, including the introduction, has been written solely by the author, and attribution of authorship to any other writer, whether living or dead, is in no manner intended.

The Macmillan Company, New York

Collier-Macmillan Canada Ltd., Toronto, Ontario

Printed in the United States of America

CONTENTS

Introduction

BY N*RM*N M**L*R

YOU MAY WELL BE WONDERING WHAT I'M DOING OUT HERE cutting somebody else's grass. Alien corn would be more like it. There may even be some (I'd bet my Bobby button on it) whose sinuses have long since backed up with thick green envy and are primed and ready to disgorge their load at the slightest sign that I'm losing my cool. Pull their chain and what do you get: "He'll do anything for a buck!" If you're man enough to step out back and repeat that, fine; if not, shut up and hear the word.

Suddenly last summer this hick approaches me. He comes on smelling prodigiously of the stockyards, Rush Street, the underside of White Sox bleachers, Carl Sandburg and other definitive Chicago pollutions. By cracky, he's written a cute little book of parodies and thinks it would be super if I'd dash off an equally cute little introduction for it. I indicate with a gesture not widely used in convents just what I think of him and his book. But this is a persistent hick, maybe even a sly hick, and as he moves in to press the assault I catch a whiff of his real musk: a touch of City Hall behind the ears; the barest hint of Shameless No. 5 by LBJ on the pulse.

Quoth the hick: "But you are our nation's greatest living writer, are you not? You are Nat Hawthorne come back on a Honda to save us all. Is it wrong of me to seek the morning star? Should I settle for Styron, maybe? Or Algren? Or mince along the tightrope with Barth and Nabokov? Forgive me, sir, for disturbing you. I have been grossly misled. I was told that you ran with the underdog; that unlike Miss

3

McCarthy you occasionally had converse with us woolly folk from the great Midwest. I had been far better advised to approach the altar of Capote. They say he's very thoughtful and considerate now."

That's how it happened, Clyde. Nobody likes to step on caterpillars. It's not that they deserve more consideration than, say, ants, but they leave the damndest mess on your shoe. What could I do?

The less said about the book the better. But I owe it to Mother Harvard, to Dwight Macdonald and to my own volatile juices to prove that I've done my homework. According to that overpaid Boswell, A. E. Hotchner, Hemingway said that the next long step up the literary fire escape from the writing of parody is being clever on toilet walls. And, dear friends, it saddens me not one whit to report that most of the gargle in this Dixie Cup doesn't even qualify as parody. The whole slosh smells of travesty to me. Sometimes, when the author's spavined muse soars to ankle level, it graduates to the burlesque division; but it never makes the parody scene at all. That's just one man's opinion, of course. But what a man!

Wells pursues his classically purile theme (what, for goodness sake, might happen if some favorite nursery tales were to be retold by modern authors) with all the zest of a tranquilized tree sloth. The book should appeal intensely to anyone stranded on a desert island with nothing else to read, and it is nicely balanced for throwing at cats or passing congressmen.

So that you won't feel entirely cheated by Macmillan, Wells and the whole bunch who stole your nickel, I'll toss in one of my special poems. Don't sniff at it. Compared with what follows, it's a pearl beyond price.

SOME OF MY BEST FRIENDS ARE UT
GUT,
    SLUT,
      RUT.
        TUT!

The Night Thoughts
of Cinderella

BY J*M*S J*YC*

OH THEY THINK THEMSELVES SO SMART THEY DO OFF AT
the big ball in all their scraggly finery as if lace and chintz
could make silk purses out of sows ears it nearly made
me sick the way they minced and pranced through the
kitchen all of them at least five times to be sure I got
an eyeful of them decked out I hope that prince has a
strong stomach or is blind it would be a kindness to him all
of them homely as sin though I will say the gowns helped to
hide their figures all knobs and shins and tendons but they
couldnt do anything about their feet great splayed things
bulging out beneath the skirts like somebody was trying to
hide an ape in too short a bag but bad as the girls are the
old lady is worse over sixty and still trying to look like little
Bo Peep with glands all got out in red tulle and carrying a
crook the prince will think shes come as a walking great
bloody sheep theres a little shepherd in every man she says
to the girls ever so coyly when she comes down Lord what
she had better hope is that theres a little ram in every near-
sighted sheep I hear the prince is looking for a wife finally
after the king and queen gave him an ultimatum to either
settle down or pack up all his rowdy friends and get out of
the palace supposed to be a wild one he is fond of wine and
horses and chasing wild pigs but not so keen on the ladies
as he might be they say because he has some English blood
in him but handsome as the devil on wheels almost too
pretty to be a man though where he would be getting such
looks beats me if you keep the king in mind though maybe
the queen didnt

7

Well they ought to be there by now if that wreck of a coach and four was up to the big hill the castle sits on the doorman will have a hard time knowing whether to show in the horses or whats inside the carriage with a drink it wouldnt be a hard mistake to make but maybe Im just bitter though Lord knows Ive reason to be the way they treat me you are such a lucky little girl the head of the orphanage said when he handed me over to the old lady to be going to such a fine home and with a real society family my just think of all the good things youll have to eat and to wear and never have to do a lick of work from dawn till dusk Lord they had me tidying up the carriage on the way home Id like for the head to see me now and what fine greasy rags Ive got to lounge around the hearth in while I sup elegantly on their leavings thank goodness I still know a trick or two to pull on that evil minded footman just enough ankle to keep him trying sober youre too ugly to bear I always tell him but with a little gin in me I might see you in a better light I have to think up something soon as this bottle will hardly last the night might as well kill it fast and get some sleep before the harpies get back from the ball

Thats strong stuff too raw but does the job makes things look better even this place is not so bad if you shut your eyes and hold your breath and imagine wild things the way I used to do back at the orphanage some well meaning social worker had filled me up with a lot of muck about fairy godmothers and such Lord knows Id trade mine in for another bottle of gin right now still it would be nice if she would pop in and throw some heavy magic around for me a white satin gown with puffy sleeves and cut low enough in front to take the princes mind off his boyfriends and my hair dressed out to some indecent Rapunzel length and stuck all full of sequins and me fairly reeking with fancy perfume and to show off my tiny feet like a babys says the footman some crystal slippers and then into a golden coach with six white stallions to pull it so full of spirit that their hooves strike fire in the road and up that hill like it was down and maybe the castle doorman would have to call for help when he saw such a grand livery bearing down on him and out would come the prince to see together with all the ball behind him or better yet he will be dancing with one of my stepsisters trying hard not to founder on her feet when the shout comes in and he leaves her standing with her ugly mouth gaping like a chunk of liver thats been worried by a bulldog and he runs down the steps just in time to catch a glimpse of my crystal slippers twinkling out beneath the brocade as I alight and this inflames him to the point where he keels over on his royal behind in a dead swoon from which only a virgins kiss can awake him providing she is wearing crystal slippers then all the virgins in the kingdom line up to take a crack at him and the line is a lot longer than it would be if the truth were known they pass by the poor stricken lad for a week kissing him till he gets slick as an oyster and at the very end of the line is me dressed now in my regular outfit but looking ravishing in spite of all only one thing is that instead of bare feet I have on the crystal slippers then while all the others are laughing them- selves silly at the sight of me I plant a juicy one on the princes sensual even when in a coma mouth and he shud- ders like somebody slipped a chunk of ice into his tights and wakes up swearing his love for me and plighting hot troths all over the place

You should see the looks on the faces of the laughing virgins then they look like theyve just been poleaxed most specially the members of my adopted family

Behold your princess and soon to be gorgeous queen says the prince now restored to more manly vigour than he knows just quite what to do with make her your obscenities and they all have to file by and kiss the toe of my crystal slipper not that I am spiteful or enjoy it too much except when the old ladys turn comes I act like my foot is cramped and take off the slipper so that she has nothing but a pretty rancid big toe to aim for and she bucks at this and turns up her nose which is a big job by itself but the prince sees this and yells bear down there you hopeless crone and consider yourself lucky to even see the royal toe for it is as close to real class as youll ever be likely to get and by the way you and your ugly daughters are just the ones to take charge of the royal scullery and all the other filthy jobs around the palace providing my lovely princess soon to be your all powerful queen does not find you too disgusting even to have around which sounds just fine to me and we all live happily ever after.

Hansel and Gretel

BY J. D. S*L*NG*R

"PREJUDICE" IS A PRETTY NASTY WORD, NO MATTER WHAT the context, and I hate to throw it at you right here at a point where, by all standards of that yellowest of journalism which goes lurching about under the hilarious name "modern fiction," I should be courting your interest with the most pleasant and seductive words at my disposal. But compared to what I'm going to have to ask you to put up with in this story, a merely *nasty* word stands up and wiggles its behind for a pat of affection as compellingly as a blind cocker spaniel that has just given birth to a litter of stunning boxer puppies. But, as I sit here at a typewriter that, deep in its depraved, imperfectly mechanical soul, thinks that it is the true and only hope for the collective salvation of upstate New York and a good part of Long Island besides, I can see no way *not* to admit that I have a prejudice against each and every piece of prepubescent literature of the sort that begins with that wretchedly indiscriminate phrase "Once upon a time . . ."

Lest that notably vocal segment of American readership known as the "So What!" school now attempt to rest its case, let me hasten to add that what follows purports to be a fairy tale, of all things; and, to draw a diagram for this same group, most fairy tales begin with exactly that vague invitation to horror. To my mind, and its presence has been verified by seven out of ten leading mental institutions, beginning a story with "Once upon a time" is about as appropriate as if one day very early in the Civil War General Pickett had strolled up to his men and said, "You fellows

13

won't mind terribly, will you, if at some time in the future, I have to ask you to make a suicide charge?" I hope to God he didn't!

If somebody is going to turn me into a frog or a swan you can bet your sweet life that I'm going to be keenly interested in knowing when it's likely to happen. I might even go so far as to look at my wristwatch or call the local time number. Take *Sleeping Beauty* for a devastating instance. I never once read that one without going wild: the princess would wake up a hundred years from when? For all I know she might be sleeping somewhere up in Central Park right this instant, waiting for me to come along and kiss her.

Well, you won't have to worry about being a volunteer spellbreaker or a gigolo prince charming for anybody in *this* story because everyone involved is now dead. But it began at exactly 10:18 A.M., November 21, 1938, outside a house that stood (it burned to the ground in 1949) near the edge of a large state forest in Maine.

At that precise moment a fourteen-year-old boy whose name was Booker Ratchford was having trouble with the zipper of his black leather jacket. He had just come outside at the more or less direct order of his father, who had hinted that he would be greatly pleased if Booker would bestir himself to go forth and fetch some firewood from the forest. He had even gone so far as to follow Booker to the door, hand him the jacket and a stocking cap, and push him outside.

"And don't come dragging back in here with a handful of soggy twigs, Buddy," his door-slamming line had gone, "I want a lot of very large, very dry logs—as many as you and that disappearing act you call your sister can carry in here during the next half hour."

Booker finally made an uneasy peace with the zipper at a point just above his navel—it would go up no farther, but neither would Booker give it the satisfaction of starting over from the bottom—and started rummaging through the pockets of his jacket. For a long time he actually removed nothing from either pocket though it was obvious that his fingers were making a great number of extremely sophisticated tactile decisions within their linty interiors. Finally, with a jerk of triumph, his right hand emerged holding a book of matches. Booker lifted the front cover, completely ignoring its graphic invitation to enjoy the vastly superior therapeutic advantages of wearing an Ajax Truss, and from the space between the matches and the back cover, extracted a tightly folded sheet of tissue paper. This he carefully opened to reveal a message printed in large block letters by a red crayon. It said: "Donne was wrong. *You* are an island. I can't waste any more time convincing you. Good-bye. Effie."

As he read this, Booker's long, thin, certifiably El Greco face registered a deep and genuine concern. He refolded the tissue paper and stuffed it back into the pocket without bothering to put it back inside the match folder. Then he walked toward a large outcropping of rock that erupted into an impressive twenty-foot pyramid about a hundred yards to the north of the house.

Standing on the far side of the rocks he found a girl, ten years old, dressed in a faded blue coat. Effie was hatless and wore a pair of run-down saddle oxfords but no socks. Her nose was running fast enough to have interested the TVA people but she made no effort to staunch or even divert its flow. A stranger happening upon her at this moment would have noticed two things, though, before properly appreciating this nasal Niagara: whirring away in her right hand with tremendously practiced ease was a Tibetan prayer wheel of the sort always used in old Ronald Coleman movies, and, without being terribly apparent, it was nonetheless evident that her feet were about two inches off the ground.

Booker regarded his sister silently for more than a minute

then reached out and gently touched her arm. The wheel stopped spinning and Effie dropped lightly back to earth.

"What did you have to go and interrupt for?" she asked petulantly. "I was just getting warmed up."

"El Toro wants us to bring in some firewood," Booker said, "but that's not why I stopped you. Firewood I can get plenty of by myself, but I can't get a new sister and that's exactly what I'm going to be needing unless you stop this pinwheel Prometheus bit. Have you got any foggiest notion what the temperature out here is, for God's sake! No socks, no hat, and probably a pair of shorts on under that blue Kleenex you use for a coat!"

During this outburst of brotherly solicitude Effie's face struggled to remain impassive, but an expression of impatience coming up fast from the inside broke through long before Booker had finished. Partly to hide this reaction and partly because she had just become aware of its sodden condition, she started wiping her nose with the sleeve of her coat.

Booker, who misread this belated attention to basic personal hygiene to mean that he was getting his message across, laid on with renewed vigor.

"Or do you think that you're already at the place where little physical discomforts like double pneumonia and frostbite can't touch you? Because if you do, I've got news for you, a regular press-stopper: people die when they get run down and don't eat and flit around outdoors in November with next to nothing on like they were some kind of goddam White Rock Fairy! And whether you like it or not, or want to be or not, you just happen to still be a people—a plain old standard issue, Mark I human being."

By way of reply, by way of definitely *unimpressed* reply, Effie pointed to the largest of the rocks with the handle of her prayer wheel. On its broad face, carved with crude but passionate legibility was the single word EXPIATE.

"I know it's there," Booker shouted. "You don't have to

tell me it's there. I watched Hansel chisel it in, remember, while you were still sucking your thumb. He came out here on the afternoon that Gretel died and made me watch him. Then he picked up that prayer wheel that Gretel had sent off for and within a month had killed himself with it just the way you're doing right now, Sister dear. Don't you think that's enough expiating for one family?"[1]

"It isn't enough expiating," Effie said, stamping a somewhat bluish foot. "And I have to do it for both of us because you wouldn't let Hansel teach you. He told me that he and Gretel had worked it out and it would take at least a billion turns of the prayer wheel to make up for taking that little old lady's life—a billion! And that if you and I turned the wheel just as fast and as long as we could we might—just might—make a billion before we died."

In a much gentler tone of voice Booker said, "Did it ever occur to you that Hansel was some kind of a nut? I don't know what kind of slide rule he had that he could figure out how many turns of a wheel equals the life balance of a crazy woman who tried to kill somebody, but I'd sure like to get my hands on it for a minute and figure out how many turns *he* ought to have to do to make up for turning his little sister into a basket case."

Effie regarded her brother with that pitying expression

[1] For the sake of the reader who hasn't prepared himself for this story by reading every word of my previously published work, and my publisher assures me that there are still enough of you around to make this digression not only justifiable but urgent, it should be explained at this point that the Hansel and Gretel whose names have just been dropped (although the observant among you will have noticed that these names did figure fairly massively in the title of this narrative) are, or were, the older brother and sister of Booker and Effie. As Booker just indicated, they died within a month of each other, having shared a rather shattering experience. When Hansel was ten and Gretel eight (Brooker and Effie being respectively four and two), their mother died and their father remarried almost instantly. Haste, especially in choosing a second mate, frequently makes great lumbering mistakes. The children's stepmother turned out to be—to put the matter as charitably as possible—*not* the homemaking

type. She had a particular aversion to children ages ten and eight and she systematically set out to get rid of Hansel and Gretel. One afternoon while their father was away, she sent them out into the forest with instructions not to come home until they had gathered enough wild strawberries to fill a certain basket, which she gave them. Since the basket had a discrete but perfectly serviceable hole in its bottom, which the children for all their disgusting precocity did not notice, they were still looking for strawberries when it got dark, and, as their stepmother had hoped, they got quite thoroughly lost.

They passed the night as best they could, recounting to each other all the great sayings of Li Po and other great gurus who, in their innocence, they didn't recognize as the shameless fabrications of Ezra Pound, and in the morning started out again, just as lost as ever. About noon they came into a clearing and saw a little house made completely out of (and I know this may strain your credulity, but you must recognize that some of your habits strain mine) books. It turned out to be inhabited by a little old lady, who invited the children in, fed them, and after hot baths, made them go to bed with warm copies of *The Wind in the Willows* under their feet. But like all kindly people, the little old lady had a sinister motive. She was a cashiered librarian, mad as a hatter, whose demented dream was the establishment of her own library. It was to be composed of all the world's great books of wisdom, uncensored and free from the strangulating control of any narrow-minded civic or religious groups. And she had made it come true out there in the middle of a forest. Only one thing had proved lacking: no one ever came to read her books.

But all that was changed with the arrival of Hansel and Gretel. While they were sleeping, the little old lady sealed off all the doors and windows with unabridged dictionaries, issued a library card to each child, and placed it under their pillows.

During the next two years, Hansel and Gretel checked out and read thousands of books. They became the most educated and enlightened children in the world. But, naturally enough, when they had read all the books two or three times over, they became bored, began to fidget, and finally expressed a desire to leave their library home and return to the world. This, of course, threw the little old lady into a bright green panic, and when Gretel remarked that she found the library completely second rate, the proud little librarian flew completely off her hinges and attacked Gretel with a copy of *War and Peace*. Hansel, a short distance away, saw murder in the old lady's eyes and let fly with a barrage of Modern Library volumes, which dropped her in her tracks, as dead as last year's almanac.

Together, the terrified children pushed out a wall and fled. Eventually they found their way home, arriving there at sundown exactly two years to the day after their initial disappearance. As might be imagined, this so upset their stepmother that she had to stay in bed with a cold towel on her forehead for the next three days.

that little girls who *can* make their bubble gum pop reserve for little boys who can't.

"Poor old Book! You never have understood, have you? It isn't the crazy woman's life that's got to be made up, it's the *reason* for taking it that's got to be worked off."

Now it was Booker's turn to stamp his foot. He grabbed Effie's sparrow-thin shoulders (OK, that's a bit much, but have you ever seen a sparrow with fat shoulders?) and started to shake her.

"But it was self-defense, and you know it, and Hansel and Gretel knew it, and I have always known it."

Effie looked him straight in the eyes, maintaining an almost superhuman composure for one who was being shaken, and said, with such quietly powerful conviction that Booker was impressed in spite of himself, "That's right. That's exactly right. Self-defense. *Self*-defense. Having so much *self* sticking out all over you that you actually have to kill somebody else to defend it. It's the greatest sin of all—self-defense. I know it, Hansel and Gretel knew it, I have always known it, and I think it's high time that you knew it."

Booker's arms fell away from Effie and hung limply at his sides. He remained absolutely motionless. Effie looked at him for a few seconds with terrible intensity, as if she were measuring something just inside his forehead. Then she went over to the rocks, where she slid her hand into a crevice and after a moment pulled it out again grasping a shiny new prayer wheel. She came back over to where Booker still stood motionless like an erect codfish. Effie placed her own prayer wheel on the ground and put the new one in his hand. Gently she closed his fingers around the wheel's handle and began to move his arm in a circular pattern. The wheel began to turn. Effie took her hand away and the wheel continued to spin, sustained by Booker's own volition.

Looking out the window of the house a few minutes

later, a man who was definitely tired of waiting for fire-wood rubbed his eyes. He had just seen his two surviving children atop the rock pyramid at the edge of the forest. What bothered him considerably and made him think quite seriously about going for an eye examination at the very first opportunity was the fact that the top of the highest rock in the pile seemed to be about ten feet beneath the children's feet.

Goldilocks and the Three Bears

BY T*NN*SS** W*LL**MS

FITSCHEN

A Trauma in One Act

Specifications: The right half of the stage is occupied by a two-story frame house. The interior can be viewed directly and completely since the entire front is missing, as if a giant child had lifted away the wall of her doll house. The rooms are well lighted and furnished with solid but hideous department store furniture of the sort that was popular in the South during the first quarter of the century. In the living room are three overstuffed chairs: an extremely large one, one of average size and a teeny-weeny one. The kitchen is equipped with cabinets, a stove, an icebox, chairs and a table set for three. The second floor consists of one large room and is furnished with three beds, again of descending sizes. The other half of the stage is a dense forest, hung with Spanish moss and choked with underbrush. A narrow path of crushed white stone runs along the edge of the stage in front of the forest. The path terminates at a set of concrete steps that lead into the side of the house at approximately stage center.

SCENE I
Six o'clock of a summer evening

As the curtain goes up, the set is absolutely still. There is a light in each room of the house but no one can be seen. The forest behind the moderately illuminated path fades away into utter darkness. This static condition holds for one minute, then an owl hoots—twice. Another thirty seconds of silence. A white rabbit runs onto the path from the left. It proceeds about ten feet toward center then

23

stops, looks at the audience and wriggles its nose. Abruptly, the rabbit runs off the path into the forest. Immediately the owl hoots twice again and something is heard to plummet down through tree branches and hit the ground with savage impact. There is a tiny, almost imperceptible animal scream, such as a rabbit might make having just been plummeted upon by an owl. The curtain comes down, slowly.

SCENE II
Ten minutes later

The set is unchanged. Again everything is perfectly still. (Note: At this point it may also be necessary to admonish the audience that they, too, must remain quiet lest they spoil the effect.) A young girl comes skipping onto the path. She moves to the exact spot where the rabbit entered the forest. She stops there and turns toward the audience. She is a remarkably pretty girl of about twelve, with radiantly golden hair, which cascades down behind her head, falling almost to her waist.

GIRL: [*pouting prettily and stamping her foot twice to remind the audience that the owl hooted twice in Scene I*]: Where can that silly ol' rabbit have gotten himself to? [*She turns and faces the forest, cupping her hands to her mouth to form a crude megaphone.*] Here, Bunny-Bunny! I know you're in there, you naughty thing. Come out this instant, sir! Do you hear? It's getting late and Mother's going to throw a royal blue fit if I'm not back in time for dinner. Come, see what I've got for you.

She has nothing but holds up her closed right hand as if it did contain something and moves it slowly back and forth. She remains quiet, listening intently. After a few seconds she is answered by the owl, this time with but a single, satiated hoot.

GIRL: Oh, shut your beak, you silly ol' bird. You don't scare me. I know owls don't hurt people. They only eat snakes, small rodents and . . . rabbits . . .

She breaks off suddenly, stiffens and shudders. Slowly she turns back toward the audience. Her face is wreathed in smiles.

GIRL [*giggling*]: I guess that'll teach ol' Bunny to mind me. Always hopping around so smug, proud of being snow white. I wonder if I came back tomorrow in the daylight if I might be able to find a foot or something . . .

Again she breaks off as she notices the house at the end of the path. She runs toward it, steps off the path to peer into a side window, then comes back to the path, climbs the steps and tries the door. It opens and she tiptoes into the living room.

GIRL: Yoo-hoo! Anybody home?

She waits near the door, poised to run if anyone should answer. After a moment she relaxes and walks slowly about the room, opening drawers, reading letters, fingering things. Finally, when she has tried everything, she goes to the largest of the three chairs and sits down.

GIRL: Goodness, this is a hard ol' chair! Reminds me of the one Daddy used to have at our house before he ran away to Pascagoula with Aunt Rachel. Whatever happened to that chair? I was only four or five then but I'll bet I can remember. [*She closes her eyes and sits bolt upright, moving her hands in front of her in the manner of a swimmer doing the breast stroke.*] Oh yes, Mother cut it all up one day with a razor blade. She let me help a little, too, with a penknife. That was fun, especially when we pretended just what part of Daddy we were cutting.

She gets up and goes to the second chair. She tests it with her fingers, then falls into it, languorously.

GIRL [*singing softly*]:

> Bye Baby Bunting,
> Daddy's gone a'hunting,
> To get a little rabbit skin,
> To wrap his Baby Bunting in.

She draws her knees up under her chin, turns slightly sideways, presses her head deep into a corner of the chair and commences to suck her thumb, greedily. She holds this attitude for a few moments then jumps up and goes to the third and smallest chair.

GIRL [*angrily*]: That wasn't at all right—too bright, too dry, too scratchy.

She throws herself violently into the little chair, which immediately gives way beneath her. Pulling herself free of the mess of stuffing and protruding, quivering springs, she wanders into the kitchen, where she is quickly attracted by three bowls of porridge on the table. The largest bowl is still steaming hot. She picks up a spoon and engorges a huge mouthful. Her face turns beet red and she is obviously in great pain, but she retains and swallows the porridge.

GIRL: My, that was fun! Made me feel good all over. But I'd better not take any more. Mother would be sure to see the blisters and make me go to that horrid Dr. Travers and he'd want to know why my pupils are dilated.

She tries the second bowl of porridge but frowns in disgust after a single taste. Moving to the third bowl, she tests again, then eats rapidly until nothing remains.

GIRL: There, that ought to make a good splash in case I have to throw a vomit tantrum for Mother when I get home late.

She walks out of the kitchen into the hallway, sees the stairway and climbs to the second floor. With a yawn she throws herself onto the largest of the three beds, but after a few seconds of squirming, gets up and flops down on the middle bed. It has a feather mattress into which she sinks slowly but deeply. With a cry of alarm she scrambles free and gets into the third bed. This is evidently to her liking, for she stretches out at full length on her back, arranges her hair fanlike on the pillow and begins to sing softly:

I'm dreaming of a white symbol,
Just like the one my mother used to have . . .

[*Curtain*]

SCENE III
Seven o'clock the same evening

Setting the same. Three bears, walking upright, enter the stage on the path and approach the house. They are ordinary North American grizzlies—a large male, a female and a cub. The male walks with a slight limp and carries a quart bottle of whiskey in his right forepaw; the female is very nervous and frequently glances back over her shoulder to see that the cub is following, which he does, but periodically, as his mother's glance leaves him, he sticks out a long, pink tongue at her haunches. The male pauses at the foot of the steps and takes a long pull at the whiskey. He takes the bottle away from his mouth and shakes it upside down—empty. With a grunt he hurls the bottle in a high arc back into the forest. We hear a muffled thud, then an aborted hoot.

FEMALE BEAR: Big Pappa Bear, that's the third quart you've had today. You promised you would stop all this drinking before supper.

MALE BEAR [*lurching up the steps and into the house*]: I stopped, didn't I? Besides, what makes you think that mess out there in the kitchen is supper? I want meat!

CUB [*in a malicious singsong while skipping up the steps*]:

> That's right,
> We want meat!
> Lots and lots of good red meat.
> All the meat that's fit to eat,
> Even if it's not so neat,
> We know what Pappa Bear likes to eat!

FEMALE BEAR [*cuffing the cub*]: Hush your filthy little snout. Don't you make fun of your daddy.

MALE BEAR [*seeing the wrecked chair*]: Oh that's a pretty mess, all right! [*He glares accusingly at the female.*] When did you manage to do that? After we went out? I thought you were a long time catching up. Just a little fit to tide you over till evening? You're a great mother, you are, jealous of your own flesh and blood. No wonder that I take a little drink now and then or that the cub's not right. . . . Living with a furniture-clawing maniac, for God's sake!

FEMALE BEAR [*sobbing*]: That's not true. I didn't do it this time, I swear I didn't do it!

CUB [*from the kitchen*]: She's made a mess out here, too, Big Pappa, and eaten all my porridge. [*Both adult bears run into the kitchen.*]

MALE BEAR [*disgustedly*]: You don't do things halfway, do you, woman! Tear up his things and eat up his food. You're straight out of a textbook.

FEMALE BEAR [*near hysteria*]: I didn't do it, I tell you. [*Points a shaking paw at the smirking cub.*] He did it, don't you see, to make it look as if I had another spell.

CUB [*rolling his eyes and letting his jaw hang slack*]:

> Oh no, Mother dear, not me,
> My IQ's only twenty-three!

The female lunges for the cub, who scoots under the table for protection; then, as she closes in on him, he makes a dash for the stairs. The female follows, and the male, slowed by alcohol, gropes around for a weapon in one of the kitchen drawers. After a few seconds he finds a pair of scissors and follows his wife up the stairs after the cub. Above, the cub has stopped at the entrance to the bedroom and stands staring at the girl sleeping in his bed at the far end of the room. The female is about to seize him when she, too, sees the girl and stops. But the male, too far gone to take in anything quickly, stumbles past both of them into the room.

MALE BEAR [*brandishing the scissors*]: Don't lay a paw on that cub, woman, or so help me, crippled as I am, I'll . . .

He breaks off, seeing the girl at last. He stands stock still, peering thickly at her sleeping form, still holding the scissors raised above his head. The girl wakes up, looks with horror at the big bear, then screams and jumps out of the far side of the bed and hurls herself through the open window. The three bears rush to the window and look down. The girl is lying in a twisted heap on the steps leading into the house. The bears turn and run back downstairs, with the cub leading the way. He pushes open the door with difficulty as the girl's body is blocking it. The girl is conscious but unable to move. The older bears arrive and the female bear leans down and tries to make the girl more comfortable.

FEMALE BEAR [*gently*]: Why did you jump out of the window, little girl? Did you think we would eat you up?

CUB [*hopping excitedly from paw to paw*]: We still could, you know. Eat her, I mean.

MALE BEAR [*considerably sobered*]: Your mother's right— you have got a filthy snout. [*He deals the cub a mighty slap, which knocks him off the steps.*] Besides, you know we don't eat people, just other bears.

GIRL [*weakly*]: It wasn't that at all. I just woke up and saw this huge figure standing over me with scissors, and I thought it was my Daddy come back to cut off my hair like Mother always said he would if I was naughty.

The bears look at each other, plainly baffled. The girl is dying. She gasps for breath. The bears lean over her, straining to hear what she will say next.

GIRL [*barely audible*]: It might have been rather nice . . . being eaten . . . just like ol' Bunny.

[*Curtain*]

The Three Pigs

BY *V*L*N W**GH

"MY DEAR," SHOUTED LORD OLIVER PRIZE-UTTERLY PIG AT his cousin Percifal, who was sitting in a lawn chair in front of his new house, "what a too-different sort of place you have built."

At the shout Percifal looked up from the book on mummification rites he was reading just in time to see Lord Oliver's silver grey Austin-Healey leap the curbing of the drive, plough through the rose arbour and spend the last of its considerable momentum against the potting shed.

"You ought really to remember to switch off the ignition when you park, Oliver," Percifal said, getting up to greet his visitor, "or at least to disengage the gears. Those were some of my best cuttings."

"Oh, I never shut it off," Lord Oliver responded wearily, sinking into Percifal's chair and tossing the book away under the lawn sprinkler. "It's very bad for the motor to be continually starting and stopping it. I'm sorry about the roses, though I doubt that the shed is much of a loss. Who did the house for you, by the way? It seems to be made of straw."

"A chap named Wolf designed it," said Percifal, ducking under a stream of water to retrieve his book. "He has offices in the West End and everyone's going to him. Supposed to be the latest thing, straw. Never needs paint, you know."

"I can see that," Lord Oliver said, "but what about rain, wind and cold, not to mention fire? I suppose you have insurance?"

"Wolf handles that, too. Very reasonable. Fire is the only real nuisance. He won't cover you if you smoke." Percifal looked proudly at the house. "Would you care to see through it?"

"Thank you, no," Lord Oliver said. "I suffer from hay fever, as you might have been good enough to remember. I really don't see how I can visit you at all now and you know how fond I am of your Port."

"What a pity," said Percifal. "I should have thought of that when I talked to Wolf. I could have had it made from sticks and mud. That's also going quite well this season. As a matter of fact, my brother Simon has just had Wolf run up one like that for him."

"Simon's Port is wretched," said Lord Oliver, sulking. "Why couldn't you have had a regular brick home like mine?"

"Wolf would never use brick. He doesn't work with artificial materials; thinks it's a betrayal of the architect's trust. Bricks aren't found in nature." Percifal fished round in his pockets until he found a scrap of paper. "Perhaps you'd like to talk to Wolf about a new house for yourself? Here's his number."

"Wouldn't dream of it," Lord Oliver said, leaping to his feet. "I can't imagine what's gotten into you and Simon, to be taken in by such a scoundrel. And now, if you'll be good enough to get your potting shed off the bonnet of my car, I shall be going."

.   .   .

Percifal rang up Wolf.

"My cousin Lord Prize-Utterly needs a new house. He's terribly bad at business and asked me to handle the details with you."

"Good-o!" said Wolf. "What shall it be?"

"Well," said Percifal, "straw is out for him and I doubt

that sticks and mud would suit his station. He's in the Government, you know, and does a lot of entertaining. What else have you?"

"We're doing some very smart things with sod and clamshells," said Wolf.

"That somehow doesn't sound right for him, either," said Percifal. "He'll want something impressive."

"I've just the ticket, then," said Wolf, "old bottles filled with varicoloured sand and then fused together. Makes a stunning appearance and gives very low maintenance."

"But bottles aren't found in nature, are they?" Percifal asked.

"Look round Hyde Park any morning," Wolf said, "more of them than there are flowers, I'll tell you that."

"That's it, then," said Percifal, relieved. "I'll leave the rest to you. Lord Oliver is only anxious that work should start as soon as possible."

Percifal rang off and went outside to smoke.

.   .   .

The Hadley Swines were the last to arrive. Oliver came out to meet them in the hall under the grand staircase.

"What a beautiful chandelier," said Lady Swine. "Your house is divine. They simply don't make them like this any more. Beats 10 Downing all hollow and Hadley refuses to let me do it over. Says it would militate against the new austerity programme he's working up."

"Quite," said Sir Hadley.

"Nice of you to come," said Oliver, preening himself. "Dinner is just to be served."

Forty heads bowed as the Archbishop intoned the grace.

Forty heads lifted sharply as the first great blow of the wrecking ball struck the wall of the dining room.

Rumplestiltskin
the Goldmaker

BY S**L B**LL*W

WHEN I THINK HOW I GOT INTO THIS MESS WITH THE QUEEN
it really makes me want to cry. I could kick myself.
Me, at my age, getting tender-hearted and trying to make
like a human being.

Before you get out your violin let me give you a few
facts about myself. I'll be brief because I know that facts
make tedious reading and I can't tell you how much I want
you to hear me out. So pull up a chair, lean back and keep
reminding yourself how very hard I'll take it if you fall
asleep.

So, OK? My name—which has more to do with this
story than you might suppose—is Rumplestiltskin. A real
handle, I'll admit. And I'm a gnome, Bavarian stock, who'll
never see the sunny side of six hundred again. Don't let
the age throw you, some facts are just harder to take than
others. And, in case you haven't been moving in gnome
circles lately, you should know that for us that's getting on
in years. I had a great-uncle who made it—just barely—
past seven hundred, but my mother always said that he had
a lot of sylph in him and that I shouldn't count on anything
like that, especially if I kept on tearing around the Black
Forest every night as I was in those days. But that's another
story and I'm not sure if I'm going to have the time to finish
this one.

What you need to know right here is that there are certain ground rules for being a gnome. Most of them are
pretty routine: don't look a toad in the eye, never let a
mortal find out your real name, stay out of churches—stuff

like that. After a while you never give them a second thought. Who really wants to look a toad in the eye, anyway?

In any case, they're a small enough price to pay for the privileges we enjoy. And I don't want you to get the wrong idea about me. I'm not a whiner. Oh, no! About most things I'm a prince. Ask any of my colleagues. "Rumplestiltskin never complains," they'll tell you. I've never minded being old and gnarled, for instance; even as a kid. I had a happy childhood really. You soon learn to handle the kidding that people dish out. I mean regular people. Sure, they're better looking for a while. It used to bother me to have them forever crossing themselves or throwing salt over their shoulder when I'd go by, but I've survived.

So—where did I go wrong? I'll give it to you straight. What caught up with me was one of those quiet, sneaky little rules that until you're about five hundred you never give a second thought to. It's right there on page 1, line 1: "Gnomes under no circumstances may do something for nothing." Sounds harmless enough, doesn't it? And it certainly accounts for the fact that the world is full of rich old gnomes. But silly as it may seem, it turned out to be the one thing I couldn't live with.

My fiasco with the Queen—you shouldn't think it's the first time I've been on thin ice. But I promised to be brief so you'll just have to take my word for it that this particular problem has been bugging me for a long time. Before, I've always managed to pull out of it but this time, I'm afraid, I cut it just a little too close.

This particular mess began about ten months ago. I was sitting in the local tavern one evening—one of the few places, by the way, where nobody seems to care if you're a gnome—when in comes the village miller for his nightly snootful. He's got the biggest mouth since Peter the Hermit, and, in addition, he brags more than Casanova. He can't stand to be topped, a fact well known to everyone, espe-

cially the tailor, who's no gem himself. The tailor special-
izes in putting the miller on, just to see what new type of
asininity he'll come up with. He waits till the miller is about
half-crocked and this time the tailor decides he'll start the
ball rolling by boasting about how smart his son is. This is a
laugh really, because the kid can't find his own nose in the
dark. But the miller goes for it like Abelard went for Hélo-
ïse (excuse the namedropping, but I really have been
around). His daughter, the miller shouts, is so smart that
she can make butter out of skimmed milk. The tailor says
that's nothing, his boy can milk a cow with his feet (probably because the poor soul thinks that's the right way to
do it). The miller counters that his daughter can make hens
lay up to six eggs in one day and the tailor, enjoying it all
hugely, trumps this by saying that it's a poor day when his
son can't get an even dozen per hen. By this time the miller
has worked up a full head of steam. He gets red in the face,
jumps up on the table and screams that his daughter can do
something that nobody else in the world can do. The tailor
pulls a solemn face and looks impressed.

"And what might that be?" he asks.

"She can make straw into gold," yells the miller, "any-
time she wants to."

Well, of course, everybody in the place breaks up at this
and starts hooting the miller. Everybody, that is, except me
and another character who's been sitting back in the corner
taking all this in. He's one of the King's spies, of course. I
know most of them, as they've been keeping an eye on me
for years. And right away I know the miller's daughter is in
bad trouble.

This King of ours is not exactly what you'd call an enlightened monarch. He's interested in just two things: gold
and girls, in that order. He'll go to any lengths to get his
hands on either and it was the job of his spies to report all
the possibilities, no matter how preposterous.

Sure enough, about two days later a couple of the Royal

Guard show up in the village and with their customary tact simply put the snatch on the miller's daughter and carry her off to the castle before she knows what's hit her. I watched them gallop away with her tied across an extra horse like a bag of meal.

And right there's where I made my first mistake. I have this little voice inside me that pops off every once in a while. A conscience, I guess people would call it, and it told me that I should feel sorry for the kid. It wasn't her fault that her old man was a blowhard. She'd last about five minutes with the King. It wasn't that she was a pretty girl, far from it. The King wouldn't give her sort a second glance. That wasn't it. But if she couldn't make straw into gold he'd dispose of her pronto. And that, said my little voice, should bother me.

I managed to stall it off for a few hours but in the end it got to me. It bothered me so much that I passed a little transportation spell that put me in the castle dungeon where the miller's daughter—her name was Gwendolyn, of all high-sounding things—was crying her eyes out. The King had packed the place with straw, locked the door and told her to get cracking. And I guess it didn't help matters when I materialized on her. I've been working for years on a way to do it more gradually, but it doesn't seem to help much. Gwendolyn screamed and fainted dead away.

By the time she came around I had about half of the straw made into gold; it's no trick, really, when you've got really first-class straw. But at my age nothing goes as easily as it used to and this was stable straw—used—and it was a messy job.

I hadn't forgotten the rule about not doing something for nothing so when Gwendolyn had pulled herself together I told her that while I was happy to be able to help her out of this little jam, I'd have to have a tiny something in return.

"Like what?" she asked, suspiciously.

It flattered me for a second to think that she was worried

about me—I don't really look my age. But then I remembered what her home must be like—life with father—and I put it down to pure reflex.

"Anything will do," I told her. "How about that ring you've got on?"

It was a crummy ring, actually, but you'd thought she was parting with the Star of India the way she carried on about giving it up.

"Look, girlie," I said, "this is no drill we're involved with here. This King plays rough. If you want me to finish this job so both of us can get out of here with our necks you'd better hand it over."

It probably hurt my little voice to see me play it that way, but the girl was dumb and I had my gnome self to think about. She gave me the ring finally and I got back to work on the straw, congratulating myself on having managed to save Gwendolyn, fox the King and stick to the rules all at the same time.

As it turned out I hadn't foxed anybody but myself. The King charges in and goes berserk at the sight of all the gold. It drove him wild. Instead of letting Gwendolyn go as he'd promised, he sends for more straw—even filthier—and tells her she's got to do an encore. She's crushed, of course, and in my hiding place behind the gold, I practically had a fit.

Well, there was nothing to do but go through the whole bit again. This time I made Gwendolyn fork over her dirty handkerchief in payment—it was all she had, other than her dress. But while I whacked away at the straw I gave the situation a little thought. The King's greed knew no bounds, as they say—he'd keep me at it till all the straw in the kingdom had been turned into gold. And, little voice or no little voice, I just wasn't up to that sort of work, even if it meant that Gwendolyn got the ax. We had to have a plan.

"When his nibs comes in again," I instructed Gwendolyn, "tell him that this is it—no more—you're out of gas, and that if he doesn't let you go, all the gold will turn back into straw. It won't, of course, I don't do cheap work, but he doesn't have to know that."

I thought I had the King in a corner for sure but I was wrong again. In addition to being greedy and lecherous, he's sly. Gwendolyn speaks her piece pretty well and it scares him all right, but he thinks for a minute and then comes up with a real nasty proposition. If she will do just one more batch for him, he tells her, he'll marry her and make her his queen and they'll live happily ever after with all that gold. Right then, I can tell you, I felt like throwing my weight around a little. But, of course, I couldn't. It would have been the end for both of us. I just hoped that Gwendolyn would stick to her guns.

I've got to give the King credit. He knows more about women than I'll ever know and I can spot him five centuries. Gwendolyn went bug-eyed at the thought of being Queen. You could practically see her stupid little peasant heart drooling at the prospect. She was already planning a triumphal return to the village. She tells the King it's a deal and in comes the straw—tons of it.

"You'll help me just this one more time?" she purrs at me as soon as the King's gone. "I just couldn't say no."

"That's getting to be the story of my life," I told her. "You're a real pal. You've stretched your luck and I ought to let it snap back in your face."

Then she starts to moan and cry and throw herself around on the straw till my little voice can't stand it.

"OK," I tell her. "I'll bail you out one more time, but you've got to pay me something—that's the rule."

Now it's Gwendolyn's turn to get sly. The world's full of skunks, do you know that?

"You gnomes must get lonely," she says, "living all by yourselves for hundreds of years at a time. I'll tell you what I'm going to do. I doubt that the King and I will have much time for children for a while so when our first baby comes along I'll give it to you. You can raise it as your own."

Can you beat that! This piece of utter depravity from the poor little helpless thing I'd been knocking myself out to save from the King's evil clutches. If ever two people deserved each other, they did. I couldn't even bring myself to speak to her. I grunted and set to work. I made the straw into the cheapest gold I could (lots of air pockets) and cut out of there fast. She didn't even bother to thank me.

Back home in my hut I had a few well-chosen remarks for that little voice of mine, all of which boiled down to "Shut up and keep shut." It did, and after a few months I managed to forget about the whole business. It wasn't the first time, as I mentioned, that I'd made a jackass of myself trying to help human beings.

I may have forgotten but not everybody had. Things have a way of getting around. Gwendolyn—excuse me— Queen Gwendolyn must have spilled the whole works to the King. I can imagine just how it went: "Now that we're married, George, there are one or two little things I ought to tell you." She was probably worried he'd go back on his word and order up another dungeonful of gold.

But it wasn't the King I was worried about. I had broken one of the rules and thought I could get by with it. I should have known better. It took them a while but the committee got word of it and sent a little delegation to call on me. I explained matters to them as best I could but they weren't a terribly understanding bunch. Absolute power had gone to their heads, absolutely.

"Look, fellows," I said finally. "I goofed—that's all there is to it. But I can promise that it won't happen again. I've learned my lesson."

But they wouldn't buy that. Finally I had to tell them about the baby business—what the Queen had offered. I was ashamed to bring it out in the open but it was all I had going for me. The committee has ultimate authority in cases of this kind and they don't mess around. I was on hand when they came to settle up with a friend of mine who had wandered into a church one day by mistake (he thought it was an art gallery) and they shriveled him up on the spot.

I was pretty well resigned to the same fate. I mean, when you play with fire . . . But they tossed me a line. If what I said was true, then all I had to do to square things was go and collect the baby from the Queen.

"What baby?" I asked. I've always been the last to hear.

It seemed that Gwendolyn had just had a son and that the King was mad with joy, never having had a legitimate child before, much less a son and heir. There was a big celebration going on up at the castle. The committee looked at me significantly, if you know what I mean, and said they'd hang around till I got back with the kid.

Well, that threw me, of course. I didn't want to get shriveled on the one hand, but I didn't want a baby, either. As a matter of fact, I can't stand kids. They drive me wild. But what was I to do?

"Little voice," I said to myself, "I hope you see where you've got us." There wasn't any answer.

There isn't any point in dragging this out. I can see you squirming. Nobody bleeds for a gnome, I know. But just hang on a few minutes longer.

I had no choice. I forced myself to go to the castle and claim the baby from the Queen. Quite a change there was in her, too. No more Gwendolyn the miller's mousy daughter. Still homely as sin but she's all dolled up in a satin gown with a train yet. Very haughty; very much the big deal. Tough, too. Tough as nails. She didn't even flinch when I materialized and I came on strong, I can tell you, feeling the way I did.

"What can I do for you, Jack?" she says, cool as a Vatican monsignor.

I explained the whole situation to her—everything—and she didn't bat an eye.

"Sorry about that," she says, "but I really don't see how

I can help you. If it was just me I'd give you the brat and say good riddance but he's the apple of George's eye. He'd never forgive me."

"Queen," I said, "you don't seem to understand. They're going to fry me if I don't come back with the kid. Just let me borrow him for a week or two until this thing blows over and I'll bring him back, good as new."

"Hard cheese," she tells me. "I can't do a thing for you."

I could see she had no sympathy to rouse so I decided it was about time for me to start playing the fox. There's only one way to handle this sort of dame—a lesson I learned from the King.

"Look," I said confidentially, "I'll make you a deal. I know you're rich and I know you're Queen. But there's one thing you're not, and that's beautiful. I don't mean to be rude, but behind all those fancy duds you're still just a peasant. It sticks out all over you. If you'll excuse the expression, you just ain't got any class."

She wasn't taking this very well. In fact, she was just about to ring for the troops, so I hurried on.

"You saw me turn straw into gold but what you don't know is that I can just as easily turn you into the most gorgeous creature ever born. How'd you like to look like Cleopatra, for instance, or Helen of Troy? Real class, both of them. You decide."

I was on the right track, it was easy enough to tell. Her eyes glazed over and her mouth puckered into the same greedy little "O" it had made when the King offered her the queenship. It was time to pull the string.

"If you can guess my name in the next three hours I'll make you into the classiest, most ravishing beauty the world has ever seen. You can have all the guesses you can make in three hours and call in all the outside help you want. It'll be a breeze for a smart queen like you. But, in the offchance that you don't guess my common, everyday name, then you have to let me have the kid. OK?"

She just had to go for it and she did. I don't mind telling you that I was one pretty relieved gnome. Nobody in the kingdom knew my name—that was one rule I'd never even come close to bending—and she couldn't guess it in a million years. My only worry was the committee. I just hoped they'd wait for three hours before turning on the heat. Patience is not one of their strong suits, either.

Meanwhile the Queen was sending out for name books, learned sages and the like, getting ready for the contest. Suddenly she stops and frowns.

"Wait a minute," she says, "how do I know you'll admit it if I guess the right name?"

What a bitch! Suspicious after all I'd done for her. But of course you couldn't really expect somebody like her to believe in promises. I was in no position to quibble. She did have a point.

"Here," I said, "I'll write my name on this piece of paper and if you haven't guessed it when the time is up, you can check up on me. But please, let's get going. No more delays."

"Sam?" said the Queen, swinging into action. "Louis? Algernon? Percival? Lancelot? Moses? Augie? ..."

She didn't even have a system, the poor broad. She was just going to flail around. Not a chance. I had her cold. The learned sages were scribbling out lists and feeding them to her with worried looks. It wasn't going to be quite so cosy for them around the castle if they flunked this and they knew it.

I sat down next to the baby's crib and cleaned my fingernails. From time to time I tossed a negative nod at the Queen, just to show that I was listening. To tantalize her I unfolded the scrap of paper with my name on it and acted like I was reading it, moving my lips in a misleading way. A couple of sneaky sages started edging around behind me to cop a peek but I was too fast for them. And it was then—just as I was folding the paper and putting it back in my pocket—that my little voice decides to speak up.

"I guess you think you're pretty smart, huh?" it said in the snottiest tone imaginable. "You jerk! You've painted yourself into a corner this time, Rumplestiltskin. You've slammed the door on your own clumsy fingers. I could have saved you but you told me to shut up and I did."

I guess you've had that sensation: knowing that you've just done something catastrophically stupid but you can't for a second or two figure out just what it is. I broke out in a clammy sweat and the Queen must have noticed it and took it to mean that she was getting warmer.

"Terry?" she yelled at me. "Larry? Barry? Harry? Cary? . . ."

Then it hit me, what I'd done. Just fixed it so I couldn't win, that's all. You're way ahead of me, I'm sure. I couldn't let the Queen see the paper to prove I'd won. She'd have my name and that was as much poison to the committee as the rap I was trying to beat. A frying pan fire case if there ever was one. I'm a born loser.

"You're so right!" my little voice said. "At least be a graceful one and get it over with."

The Queen was beginning to wear down a bit. She looked a little green around the gills. You could tell she was probably beginning to think about that dungeon.

"Harold?" she pleaded, going alphabetical at last. "Herbert? Hubert? Gus?"

"That's it," I shouted, jumping up. "You've nailed me: Gus the Gnome. How'd you ever guess?"

"Never mind the small talk," said the Queen, regaining her natural disposition instantly, "just pay up and get out. Helen of Troy will do."

Now I had no idea what Helen of Troy looked like—she was before my time—but I figured nobody else did either, so I just passed a standard blonde spell and let it go at that. Then, while everybody was ooh-ing and aah-ing, I slipped away. Gwendolyn wouldn't find out she was bowlegged until she went to bed. It was a petty thing to do, I'll admit, but small people have to fight in small ways.

So here I am, back in the tavern waiting for the shoe to fall. It won't be long. Our committee's nothing if not efficient. Thanks for listening. It's been a great help getting it off my chest like this. And, who knows, maybe you'll profit from my misfortune. Write a book about me. If you do, make it clear, will you, that I finally learned the biggest lesson life's got to offer: it's not how you play the game; it's whether you win or lose.

Peter Rabbit

BY J*HN *PD*K*

McGregor's wall is high. Its rough bricks are held rigid by mucus-colored mortar, each strip of which seems to exude a personal malignancy so that Peter, walking close beside it, feels subjected to the bad breath of a thousand rusty mouths. The wall also makes perceptible its thickness though Peter, except in dreams when he has followed the wailing harp of his father's voice through a hundred aching, sheet-drenching nights, has never been through it. Sometimes, in the dream geography which his fever-fertiled imagination creates beyond the wall, Peter has glimpsed his father's heavy figure, running, far ahead, staggering from crater to crater. Never gaining, Peter follows. There is no direction but a zigzag trail through the barbed wire marked with tufts of skin which decorate the cruel points with festive flags of fur. It is when Peter finds one of these, still warm and moist with his father's blood, that his mother's voice explodes the dream: "You've wet again, you wretched child!"

Twenty yards ahead, the dichotomied plumpness of their behinds creating a gyrating symphony of cottontailness, Peter's two sisters skip on toward the blackberry patch. Their tin pails, swinging, catch the forenoon sun and declaim with greedy silver mouths their readiness to receive the juice-heavy thump of the swollen berries. For a moment, remembering how the taut blue-black skins of the first picked of these will burst against the ruthless metal of the pails and deliver, with equal promiscuity, the burden of their dark milk to the questing lip, Peter feels his purpose falter and grow limp. It would be so blessedly easy *not* to do what he has sworn the steel-bright sun this day *to* do.

But his feet betray him into the hands of honor. The gate is just ahead and it stands ajar, just as in last night's dream his father's pain-cracked voice had told him it would be.

"You go on," he hears his tremulous voice call out to Flopsy and Mopsy, "I've forgotten my pail."

They turn and wave innocent acknowledgment, fully focused on the fun ahead. Peter envies them their virgin memories sealed by the membrane of time against the ravaging memory of a father they were too young to know. Of the children, he alone recalls the night when there was a someone who did not return from beyond the wall; he alone carries the growing tumor of doubt about his mother's too studied movements, too perfunctory worry, too mechanical grief. She *knew*.

On that night, long before the usual time for his father's return from his biweekly raid on McGregor's vegetable affluence, Peter recalls his mother's going out. His sisters already asleep, Peter sits reading a well-loved book. His mother, a furtive, aproned shadow, slips out of the kitchen door without a word, not knowing that Peter's umbilical eyes cannot fail to notice such a departure from routine. Then, shortly, like a guilty ghost, she comes back through the door and finishes washing the dishes. Presently, tucking Peter in, she recites her piece: "Daddy will not be coming home, I'm afraid. I think Old Man McGregor has finally caught him." This without tears, without hysteria, chillingly premature in its conviction, calm as the moonlight spilling across Peter's bed through which his mother scuttles, crablike in her shell of guilt, to bar the still expectant door. Minutes later her heartless snores smother firmly the sobs which Peter sent questing toward the moon he cannot see, the father he cannot touch.

Now Peter shades his eyes and waits until his sisters are enfolded in the verdant embrace of the woods. On the impertinent glint of a pail whose brightness will not be quenched by mere leaves, a final giggle rides back to him. Gone! Finding it harder than he imagined, Peter squeezes through the opening between gate and post. His heart alone feels too large to negotiate the space.

Inside, the wall seems twice as high and it looms in palpable and convex menace over Peter's vulnerable back. He moves quickly out of its shadow and into a patch of corn whose stalks on either side of McGregor's arrow-straight rows make an avenue which Peter, proceeding somehow, paves with fear. Though he moves slowly the stalks flash along the anxious periphery of his vision like so many frantic telephone poles viewed from a speeding train. His dream geography was less terrible than this jungle of saw-toothed green which lashes his craving for perspective with obscene rustlings and vision-aborting flappings.

Then without warning he is in the open. The transition sucks Peter's breath from the twin sacs of his lungs as surely as if he had stepped off a precipice. But it is not bright sunlight but rich shadow which covers him. Twin pillars like canted tree trunks rise up before his reluctant eyes. They are blue of a peculiar hue which Peter has never seen before and, horribly, seem animated from within, burgeoning with subtle power, as if alive.

For an old man, McGregor is astonishingly quick. His legs, still supple, bend easily when he plunges his hat earthward to cover the rabbit frozen at his feet. His aim is true and Peter's fear-flung reflex seals his never very hopeful fate. He bounds upward into the domed felt to struggle helplessly amidst a mist of acrid sweat and flurries of dandruff flakes older than himself while McGregor pouches the hat and carries its pulsing contents toward the rabbit hutch.

It is a weakness which McGregor tolerates in himself, a philanthropic concession to old age, that he can no longer find it in either ventricle of his widower's deprived heart to kill the rabbits who poach his ripe preserve. He cannot kill them but neither can he release them to ravage lettuce which brings him fifteen cents a head. So he has fashioned himself a rabbit city, cage on cage, and since he feeds its inhabitants well and moderates for them the harsher extremes of the weather, he feels himself to be a sort of denimed God of Rabbits whose omnipotence springs not from the act of creation but from the arbitrary mercy he dispenses to its teeming product.

He is stricken then, when over an empty cage, he disgorges not a quivering young lagomorph vibrant with grateful life but a corpselike form which falls heavily to the wire floor. Peter lies thus and reproaches McGregor's sense of deity with the visage of death not spared but inflicted. The old man stands there and regards his horny hands, taxing them with the charge of rabbitslaughter. The verdict: death by suffocation. But he has trapped a dozen rabbits so and finds it hard to accept the circumstantial evidence. From a slotted and copper-riveted pocket of his overalls McGregor extracts a yellow pencil. His apprehension will not support a direct touching of death and he uses the wood-encased graphite as an insulator against premature contact with that which, soon enough, he will know professionally.

Somewhere, at the very bottom of his soul's alembic, Peter feels the needling pencil point. He is not dead, the sharpness tells him, but the realization passes so slowly along his nervous system, a message to a drunken Garcia delivered on hands and knees by a blinded courier, that McGregor despairs when a much swifter messenger slides into the home plate located just behind his eyes and in the swirling dust holds up a sign which McGregor's guilt has long since expected: "Dead on Arrival."

Self-accusation, wearing cleats, tears heavy-footed across the tender turf of McGregor's sentimentality and he drops the pencil to flee to the solace of vegetable life—a sturdy carrot crying to be pulled from the obliging soil; a fat cabbage longing to be cut; an eager ear of corn waiting to disclose its golden eyes to his life-shucking hands.

Hulldown on the horizon of his consciousness Peter's bloodshot inner eye spots the delicate masts of the frigate called recognition. He thinks he hears his father's voice calling, "Peter, Peter, is that you?" But Peter, stirring languorously on the soft aftermath of shock, resents its familiar invasion of his ears as a miner trapped in total darkness is said to recoil from the first harsh rays of the rescuer's lamp.

Nonetheless, the voice, unmistakably that of his father, calls again and Peter, unable to defend the ramparts of his lassitude against the storming volume of his heart's un-bidden pounding, springs convulsively to his feet.

"Father," he croaks, "where are you?"

Endowed with the throb of real presence, freed at last of its phantom chains, the voice comes back: "Here, in the cage next to yours."

Like a seashell gone mad, the pink tissue which lines the flowerlike vertical cavities of Peter's now totally erect ears gorges with the quick blood of unbearable excitement. His father's familiar shape, deep-chested, thickly limbed, forms itself in almost perceptible distinctness beyond the flimsy cardboard partition which separates the two cages. This unseen sight flays Peter to desperate action. He looks for a weapon with which to assault the damnable opacity of the partition and finds . . . McGregor's pencil.

"Father," cries Peter, lunging forward with his yellow lance, "I'm coming."

Since the night when his wife, with an intimate laugh of betrayal, clanged shut behind him McGregor's gate, the father's heart has not once lifted as it now does in response to this brave young voice. Eyes brimming gladness he turns squarely toward its sweet source and strains against the partition which blocks him like a contraceptive from physical contact with love. It is then that the pencil point, made lethal by Peter's ardent sinews, violates the cardboard and finds quick access in the father's breast.

Peter, heartened by this easy victory, is surprised at the difficulty he encounters in withdrawing his weapon for a fresh attack. Where there should be only slight friction he feels a monstrous weight. Like a teeter-totter jarred radically off its balance, the pencil springs upward from his grasp.

"Help me, Father," Peter gasps, tugging at his perverse implement. "Push!"

But neither push nor answer comes from the other side of the partition and almost at once, in Peter's mind, a bell begins to toll the heavy notes that streaming-eyed Oedipus in his dead century must also have heard. At last, with a slight sucking sound as if a tiny mouth had slipped its salived nursing grasp, the pencil recoils free and Peter is confronted with the dripping answer to his difficulty.

"There, you see," the stained wood shouts, "it is all quite simple. No mystery at all. You simply can't expect to pull a shaft from your father's heart as easily as you put it in."

To stifle this horrid voice, to wipe away the already congealing red smirk, Peter places the pencil's point against the reproachful whiteness of the partition and moves it up and down. Endowed as it is with double powers, the pencil makes an intriguing scroll of black and crimson which Peter, in his frenzy, cannot help but increase.

He is soon beyond help. Nothing matters. The pencil gathers momentum and usurps the artist's powers. It writes. Ah, writes.

Three Billygoats Gruff

BY **N FL*M*NG

PITSCHEN

COMMANDER WILLIAM GOAT EASED HIS LEAN, MUSCULAR rump down among the heather and surveyed the bridge with apathy. There were times, increasingly frequent of late, when he despised his job. One of these days they could have back their precious license to butt and all the security mumbo-jumbo that went with it. *They*, of course, was Her Majesty's Ministry for the Preservation of Dumb Animals, Goat Branch, with headquarters in a suitably deceptive, sickeningly posh and tidy series of interconnected flats in Bloodsbury. There, scarcely more than an hour ago, William had been sitting on an impossibly scratchy carpet waiting for G (as Gruff, the head of the branch was known to those of his agents too stupid to remember his full name) to get to the point.

Points were something that old G had one hell of a time getting to. It had once taken him twelve solid minutes of wheezing circumlocution to ask William if he could spare a cigarette, and it had been a three-hour ordeal for William to extract what little information G had to reveal about this assignment. As best he could gather, two rather important animals (one of them related in a tenuous manner to the Goat of Wales) had disappeared during the past week. Both had been about top-secret Ministry business and, G had been almost certain, both had last been seen on the road leading to the bridge which William was now regarding with frowning distaste.

Quite an opposite emotion registered itself on the thick, scabrous lips which curved upward in malevolent glee under the pair of close-set, pus-colored eyes which were regarding William through a narrow slit in a hollowed-out rock across the river with the considerable aid of a pair of Russian Mark III binoculars fitted with pre-Khrushchev ground lenses.

The lips, eyes and binoculars belonged to a huge and particularly noxious troll whose passion for unroasted goat flesh and whose disgusting habit of sucking his right foreclaw after a gorge had long ago earned him the nickname Goatfinger. His real name was Malcolm and it was under his real name that he had been deported from his native Bosnia for devouring an entire flock of goats, and it was Malcolm he had to call himself in the incantation he now used to turn himself into a stunning nanny goat. If his information was correct, it would be the perfect way to throw the highly dangerous goat on the other side of the river completely off his guard and set him up for a nice, messy kill. It would be his biggest and most satisfying coup, for with this operative out of the way, nothing stood between him and all the goats in the United Kingdom.

William, completely unaware of Goatfinger's sinister scrutiny or his remarkable transformation, was hanged if he could make the bridge out to be anything other than a perfectly ordinary wooden structure over a perfectly ordinary river. Getting up, he stretched his powerful neck and cursed G for a bungling and highly uncivil servant. He had been planning something far more diverting than bridge-watching for this pleasant Sunday afternoon. A certain extremely attractive young person of his acquaintance had finally agreed to visit his flat for the ostensible purpose of examining his collection of rare tropic grasses, and William, in the amusing way he had of putting things to himself, had thought that they might make a little frantic hay while the sun shone. As it stood, he'd be lucky to get home before dinner, even if, incredibly, this wild goose chase should resolve itself immediately. If there was anything more tedious than listening to G, it was trying to tell him something and William had always to debrief himself in G's ear only. He sighed deeply as he thought of the champagne cooling itself in vain and the aphrodisical records just waiting to be played in his flat.

There seemed nothing to be gained by just standing about here in the gorse, William decided. Your ordinary goat might have reflected that there seldom was, but William's mind was geared to action, not introspection. Thinking could be dangerous in his profession. Triggerlike reflexes were the thing. He started across the bridge, his every sense suddenly drawn to bowstring tautness. He took in everything: the swirl of the water beneath him, the comforting presence of his own shadow flickering along at his right side, the number of planks he had traversed.

"Seventy-six, seventy-seven, seventy-nine," he counted softly, "ninety, ninety-one . . . Hello there, what's this!" William screamed and sprang backward as he collided with something soft and yielding in the middle of the bridge.

"Hallo yourself, big boy," said Goatfinger, in the sultry feminine voice that he had assumed along with his voluptuous shape.

"Where in blazes did you come from?" William said shakily, taking in every inch of the stunning creature before him and trying desperately to regain his composure.

"Oh, I've just been hanging around the bridge here, hoping that some handsome fellow like yourself might come trip-trapping along." As he said this, Goatfinger wriggled his shape forward and pressed his flank firmly against William's. The troll was terribly nervous and growing more ravenous by the second. He'd have to watch it or he'd break the spell and turn back into his true form before this prize morsel was sufficiently off guard.

"What's your name?" William stammered, shrinking back and away from the disturbing bodily contact.

"Can't you guess?" the wanton creature said, swinging

her hindquarters provocatively. "I've been told that even a name like Udder Delight doesn't do me justice."

"Well, I don't care if it's Udder Madness," William said archly, "I'd appreciate it if you'd stand aside and let me pass. I'm on a rather urgent secret mission."

Goatfinger's control was ebbing fast. He'd have to work quickly.

"What's wrong with you, anyway?" the troll said in a voice that was already beginning to resemble his normal croak. "The two goats who were along here last week didn't find me so hard to take."

Something thudded heavily in William's brain. It was a thought. He fought it off as he'd been trained to do, but it was no good. It overpowered the flaccid defenses of his subconscious, caromed off his cortex and shot out his mouth.

"How'd you know those goats had come this way," he shouted, bracing himself to butt.

"Because I ate them just like I'm going to eat you, James Goat," the troll shouted as he began to resume his own hideous form.

If you consult the standard spell tables in the British Museum, you will find that it takes the average troll only four-fifths of a second to cast off the effects of an incantation and regain his true shape, and Goatfinger, through much practice, had managed to cut this time almost in half. But it was still a fifth of a second too long. William took him in his just materializing midsection with a perfectly timed and delivered thrust that lofted Goatfinger cleanly up and over the bridge railing.

Everyone knows what happens when a troll falls into the water. It is not a pretty sight and even William, hardened by experience to laugh at death's more gruesome visages, found it necessary to avert his eyes from the boiling green and yellow mess below the bridge.

The thought of a moment before had saved him. Now he

gave way to a massive wave of realization. Goatfinger, in the instant of crisis, had called him James. The whole ploy —the voluptuous feminine shape, the sultry voice, the wanton manner—had been a carefully set trap for some-one named James. Well, he'd leave that for old G to puzzle out—ought to keep him busy for a month. Meanwhile he should congratulate himself on coming unscathed through a very close thing. Still, he shouldn't feel too smug. There was no way that the troll could have known that his elabo-rate booby trap would fail-fire.

William looked down at the water where one final bub-ble was just surging to the surface. "Not every mouse likes cheese, old man," he shouted down at the bubble, "nor every cat chase mice."

William turned back toward London. If he hurried, there might just still be time to meet young George at the flat.

Sleeping Beauty

BY J*HN *'H*R*

FITSCHEN

THE QUEEN WAS IN THE PANTRY, CHECKING THE GOLD SERVICE.

"Nancy," she said to the French housekeeper, "it was my impression that there were thirteen place settings of the gold but now I count only a dozen. What does your inventory show?"

"Twelve, your Highness. There have been twelve for as long as I can remember."

"Well, your memory's not very long, then," said the Queen. "The gold service was a wedding present from the Duke of Herrick and I distinctly recall its being a baker's dozen."

"You'd never have thirteen to dinner, though, would you, Mam? I mean, everyone knows that would be unlucky. So why would the Duke of Herrick send thirteen settings?"

"Nancy, you're not only superstitious, you're impertinent. If I say there were thirteen settings of the gold, then there were thirteen settings. I want the missing pieces found before noon or you may just find out that twelve is really your unlucky number."

The Queen found the King in the counting house.

"Must you always be fooling about with your treasure?" she said. "There's something I'd like to discuss with you."

"I hope it's not about that damned party you're planning for the eleven fairies," the King replied, tying up a sack of rubies. "You don't expect me to sit through an evening of that sort of chit-chat do you?"

The King sucked in his cheeks and in a prissy, falsetto

voice said, "Oh, my dear Queen, I hope the King has been behaving himself lately. We fairies are *so* concerned about the way he carries on. We hoped that marriage would settle him down. Now that you've given him such a beautiful baby daughter, we're sure that he won't go off carousing."

The King resumed his normal voice. "That's just the way it will go," he said. "I've got a good ear for that fairy talk."

"Very funny," said the Queen. "As a matter of fact, that's exactly what I want to discuss. We have a serious problem. There are only a dozen settings of the gold service in the pantry. I'm positive that originally there were thirteen and that one of the servants—probably that little French tart, Nancy—has stolen one of them. But, whatever happened to it, with the eleven fairies coming and two places for us, it leaves us one short for the christening party."

"Horrors!" said the King.

The Queen ignored this and continued, "I can't very well serve one person on silver and the rest on gold. And don't tell me that your not coming to the party is the solution. The fairies would all be mortally insulted."

"Why not switch to the silver service all around, then," the King suggested. "I've never liked eating off the gold anyway. It makes the gravy look bilious."

He paused a moment. "Incidentally, why do you suspect Nancy?"

"I thought you'd defend Nancy," said the Queen. "I heard that you were spending a good deal of time in the pantry while I was pregnant. Now I know why. You didn't pay her off with the gold service, did you?"

"You should know me better than that," replied the King. "I'll admit that I stopped off in the pantry a time or two while you were pregnant—I'm only human—but I don't set that much store by Nancy's favors, I can tell you that. The girl never washes, for one thing and for . . ."

"Spare me the details, at least," the Queen broke in. "I believe you about the place setting. You're far too miserly to part with anything with gold in it. But to get back to the subject, switching to the silver service is impossible. You and your drunken friends ruined it at the banquet following the last stag hunt. They *will* cut their meat with hunting knives! Almost every plate is ruined. Someone even went so far as to carve an obscenity into one of them. I really don't know why I try to keep anything nice as long as you insist on bringing that pack of rowdies home with you."

"They happen to be my friends," said the King, "and also some of the richest men in the kingdom. There's not one of them who wouldn't cut off his right arm for me. Or lend me money, if it came to that."

"The one who carved that filth on my silver deserves to have his right arm cut off," replied the Queen. "If they're so rich, do you suppose that one of them might have a gold service that we might borrow?"

"I dimly recall eating off gold once at old Peasely's palace," said the King, "but I wouldn't dream of asking him to loan us a place setting. He'd take it to mean that I'd been reduced to selling things off for ready cash and there'd go my credit with his bank. No. I'm afraid you're just going to have to disinvite one of those fairies. I don't know why you're so concerned, in the first place. Most of them are as old as the hills and if they ever had any magical powers, I'm sure they lost them going through the change of life."

"You must have picked up that bit of superstition from your friend Nancy," replied the Queen. "*All* the fairies are important, even if they are getting on a little. It's crucial that they all be treated well tomorrow evening. They may have magical powers and they may not, but I certainly don't intend to find out at our daughter's expense. Still, there may be something to what you say. It might be better to offend one of them outright than risk slighting them all with scratched-up silver. The question is, which one can do us the least harm?"

"Well," said the King, "you can take this or leave it

since I know you don't care much for Prince Yuri, but he says that last summer he led a hunt through the estate of that old fairy Esmerelda and she saw him riding out with four fat does. About a week later he got a letter from her to the effect that she was going to put a curse on him and his entire household. She said that the next time he pricked his finger he'd fall asleep for a hundred years—some sort of nonsense like that. I mean, if that's the worst she can come up with . . ."

"Has he pricked his finger?" asked the Queen.

"Not so far as I know," the King replied, "but what difference does that make? Obviously, if she had any real magical powers she'd have done something to Yuri on the spot, wouldn't she. If you ask me, Esmerelda's nothing but an old fraud. She's the one to weed out."

"Very well," said the Queen. "I'll send a messenger to tell her that the party's been called off. I just hope you're right."

"I'm glad you see it my way," said the King. "Now, if you'll excuse me, I've got to see to an urgent affair of state."

"In the pantry?" asked the Queen.

"As a matter of fact, yes," said the King.

Who Killed Cock Robin?

BY **A*****N R*****ND**

"Who killed cock robin?"

Never since she'd been in pigtails playing with her first trust had Desirable Mansmind so badly wanted to know the answer to a question.

Certainly her brother Percival hadn't done it. He couldn't kill a worm, much less Cock Robin, the man who, until his mysterious disappearance a few months ago, had single-handedly been wrecking the government's strangling throttlehold on the nation's economy. There was a real man and Desirable wished for the thousandth time that she had known him. Screwing her mouth into a tight "C"— for contempt—she brought her keen mind back into the present and swung her flint-gray eyes to bear directly upon the quaking figure kneeling at the side of her desk.

Even at his best Percival Mansmind was not much to look at. He was short, fat, with a classically weak chin and conformist-colored eyes which were now darting vainly about in an effort to escape the full impact of Desirable's merciless stare.

"Get up, you grub," she spat at him, "and get out of here with those tax forms. Mansmind Unlimited will not pay tribute this year or any year!"

"But Desirable," Percival gathered the courage to whine, "you're destroying the business."

"I'll give you the business, you sod!" Quick as a she-cobra, Desirable drove the sharply pointed toe of her gold pump into the roll of fat which spilled obscenely over the top of Percival's gray flannels. As she did so she couldn't help but admire the slim firmness (or was it firm slimness?) of her right leg as it lashed out.

"You've got terribly good legs, you know." Leaning back in her chair after Percival had crawled groaning out of the office, Desirable felt anew the thrill of those first words that Nails Tautummy had addressed to her. There was another man!

They'd been inspecting a section of subway track laid by Mansmind Unlimited using the revolutionary device invented by Nails. No other railroad had the guts to try it—you simply stapled the rails to the ground.

There, in the near-dark with the city rumbling above her head, Desirable had been acutely conscious of the tall figure following her down the track. Nails was tall, hard and flat, the whole of him looking like a weapon forged in stainless steel. He was wearing skintight Levis and a snug sports shirt, paper thin.

In her office chair Desirable sighed and closed her eyes. She forgot about Cock Robin; she forgot about Percival; she forgot about Mansmind Unlimited. She was totally back with Nails during that electric moment in the tunnel when the raw forces of the very earth itself had caught them up. So deep grew her absorption that her usually trigger-quick senses failed to record the slight, almost imperceptible snick of the panel that opened in the wall behind her desk.

"Nails! Nails!" Desirable writhed in the chair, oblivious. A little sound of delicious pain escaped her twisted lips. Unconsciously she toyed with the top button of her blouse —a feminine gesture she abhorred.

When Nails had said that about her legs she struck him in the mouth with her flashlight.

"Nobody gets fresh with Desirable Mansmind," she told him, drawing back her arm to strike again. But even as she said it she knew that here was a man who thrived on resistance . . . scoffed at it. He was power, he was ruthless strength, he was a coiled spring . . .

Afterward! Afterward, when all the fire and the hate and the fury were spent, they had lain quietly and put their ears to the cold metal of the tracks, hoping to hear the surging power of a distant train. Nails had made the first mistake of his life: he put his ear on the third rail.

"Nails! Nails!" Where would she ever find another man like Nails?

A whisper of sound behind her brought Desirable abruptly out of her musing. A dirty tax agent must have slipped into the office while she'd been dreaming. Well, she'd give him some gross income he hadn't been banking on! Grasping a paperweight she spun her swivel chair about.

The paperweight fell noiselessly into the deep carpet as Desirable's nervous system went into flux. Before her loomed a man unbelievably tall. He was regarding her with the handsomest sneer she'd ever seen. His hard torso, sheathed in a T-shirt and toreador pants, made her memory of Nails seem a tweedy Jackie Gleason in comparison.

"Who are you?" Desirable managed at last to gasp, her pulse throbbing near Mach II.

"Don't be stupid," the tall man said in a voice that rumbled with the humming energy of a thousand atomic reactors hooked up in series, "I am Cockney $ Robin."

When Desirable came to, she was propped up in the seat of a plane. She looked out the window and saw below her a city in flames. It was Washington!

"This is it, Desirable!" Robin stood behind her in the aisleway, looking triumphant. In his left hand he held a whiskey bottle, nearly empty; with his right he pointed at the window.

"I fixed those tax people good," he said thickly. "No more fat slugs living off my brains and my work. No more government telling me what I can't do. No more anything I don't like!"

Robin finished off the bottle chug-a-lug. "They thought I was dead, the fools, but I was only lying low, planning this little surprise."

He lurched heavily and looked lecherously down at Desirable. "You're a good lookin' woman, do you know that?" Robin lisped, beginning to drool.

What a time to talk shop, Desirable thought, disgusted.

The bottle dropped to the floor of the plane as Robin puffed out his chest and drew himself up to his full height.

"Me Robin," he grunted, thumping himself in the middle of his T-shirt. "And you're a good lookin' woman except for those skinny legs."

Robin lurched away down the aisle till he came to the door and forced it open. Furiously he thrust his great strength against the slip-stream and leaned far out, shaking his fist over the gutted city.

"There's a hot time in the old town tonight." He laughed malevolently. "How's your Great Society now?"

Desirable got out of her seat and came up behind Robin. She put one foot on the seat of his pants and pushed.

"Now I know," she thought, moistening a run in the sheer hose which sheathed the slim firmness of her right leg. "I killed Cock Robin."

Little Red Riding Hood

BY *DW*RD *LB**

A Play in One Act

SCENE I

[*The forest. A bright spring day. A gray timberwolf lurks by the side of a path. A girl, apparently about ten years old, dressed in a hooded blood-red cape, walks along the path. Her face is well back inside the hood of the cape so that we cannot see her features. She is carrying a basket covered with a white napkin.*]

WOLF [*springing out into the path*]: Just hold on there, little girl. What's the big hurry?

GIRL: So, there you are. Please stand aside, for my grandmother expects me at her cottage anon.

WOLF [*showing his teeth*]: What's your name, little girl?

GIRL: I hardly think that's any of your business. Now I must ask you a second time to step aside and let me pass.

WOLF: You're a very well trained little girl. "Never tell a stranger one's name," that's what Mummy told you—correct? Mummy's quite right. But you must have a name. I'll call you Red Riding Hood. [*He moves closer, menacingly.*] And now, Red Riding Hood, might I ask what you have in that basket?

GIRL: No, you may not. I think it's best that you let me pass at once. You're far better off not knowing what's in my basket. It's a surprise for my grandmother.

WOLF: Ah, but now you've piqued my curiosity. I'm dying to know what's in that pretty little basket of yours. Won't you lift a corner of the napkin—just a tiny bit—and let me have a peek?

GIRL: It's expressly forbidden.

WOLF: A tiny peek, that's all I want. Lift just a corner.

GIRL: Out of the question. Move aside now, I will not ask again.

WOLF: You're an exceedingly strange and exceedingly stubborn little girl. Have you no fear that I'll rip you to shreds and examine the basket at my leisure?

GIRL: None whatsoever. Wolves have never frightened me. On the contrary, it's you who ought to be afraid.

WOLF: Whatever of? A little girl in a red cape? I could gobble you up in one bite.

GIRL: You'd be biting off a great deal more than you can chew, I assure you.

WOLF: You've got spunk, I'll say that for you. You issue threats like you really mean them. I like that. If you'll show me what's in your basket I'll let you pass unmolested.

GIRL: You simply won't take no for an answer, will you? Very well. Come along to my grandmother's cottage in half an hour and you can see what's in the basket.

WOLF [*stepping aside*]: It's a bargain. In half an hour, then.

[*Curtain*]

SCENE II

[*Twenty-five minutes later. The interior of a one-room cottage. It is furnished quite simply—a bed, a table, two chairs, a wood-burning stove. The walls are made of logs crudely plastered and painted a deep red. The girl and her grandmother are seated at the table. The girl's basket sits on the table between them, still covered by the napkin.*]

GRANDMOTHER: He is coming then?

GIRL: Yes, he should be here at any minute.

GRANDMOTHER: Shall I get into bed now?

GIRL: Yes, it's time. I'll leave the door unlatched and ajar.

GRANDMOTHER: Is the woodsman nearby?

GIRL: Yes, he's working in the clearing—not a hundred yards away.

GRANDMOTHER: Good-bye, then. I never expected things to end like this.

GIRL: We've been over all that. Good-bye. [*She gets up, takes the basket and goes out.*]

[*Curtain*]

SCENE III

[*Five minutes later. Setting the same. The door of the cottage swings inward very slowly. The wolf pokes his head inside and looks about. The grandmother is in bed, feigning sleep. The wolf streaks across the room, hurls back the bedclothes, kills and devours the grandmother— all this without a sound. When he has finished, he mops up all traces of blood with a sheet, puts on the grandmother's nightcap, jumps into the bed and pulls the covers up to his chin. Immediately there is a knock at the door.*]

WOLF [*in a high voice*]: Come in!

GIRL [*comes in carrying basket*]: Hello. I've brought you your special basket.

WOLF [*still in a high voice*]: Put it down on the table and come over here where your old granny can get a good look at you.

GIRL [*going right up to the bed*]: You're not my grandmother, you're the wolf. Why are you lying in the bed? I thought you wanted to see what was in the basket?

WOLF [*in his regular voice*]: So, I didn't fool you?

GIRL: Not for a second.

WOLF: Aren't you curious to know what happened to your grandmother?

GIRL: I know what happened to her.

WOLF: Aren't you frightened that I'll eat you up, too?

GIRL: I'm counting on it. Why should I be frightened of something I know will happen?

WOLF: You're an exceedingly strange little girl. Nonetheless, I'm going to eat you. [*The wolf throws off the bedclothes and springs out of bed. The girl begins to scream.*]

WOLF [*seizing the girl in his jaws*]: Ah, when it comes right down to it you're not so brave. You're as frightened as the next one.

GIRL [*gasping*]: No I'm not.

WOLF [*sinking his teeth into the girl's neck*]: Why are you screaming then?

GIRL [*with dying breath*]: You'll find out.

[*The wolf devours the girl then goes to the table and stares at the basket. With one paw he lifts a corner of the napkin and peers inside. He leaps backward as if horror-struck*

*by what he has seen. Just as he does this a woodsman
comes running through the door. He has a large two-bladed
ax which he immediately swings on the wolf, striking him
heavily in the spine. The wolf falls to the floor, his back
broken. The woodsman prepares to swing again.*]

WOLF: Wait! Please, before you kill me, tell me what it all
means.

WOODSMAN [*bringing the ax down on the wolf's head*]:
This! [*The ax sinks into the wolf's skull and he dies. The
woodsman watches till the wolf stops twitching then he
turns to the door and shouts.*] All right. He's finished.

VOICE [*heard through the empty doorway, it sounds like
the voice of the girl, though slightly deeper, older*]:
Empty the basket then and come along. We've another
appointment to keep.

[*The woodsman frees his ax with one hand and with the
other picks up the basket from the table and turns it
upside down. A limp, gray, furry object falls to the floor
beside the wolf's carcass. It is too small to see distinctly,
but it appears to be a tiny wolf with a bloody head. The
woodsman, carrying the basket and the ax, goes out
through the door and closes it behind him. A loud belch
is heard—once, twice, three times as the lights dim and the
curtain slowly descends.*]

Jack and the Giant

BY GR*H*M GR**N*

JUAN AWOKE WITH THE TASTE OF MORTAL SIN LIKE ASHES in his mouth. He opened one eye and looked at the ceiling, where a blue fly with a gleaming, distended abdomen sat inverted watch beside a jagged crack in the adobe. Brown water oozed slowly through the crack, gathered itself reluctantly into globules and splatted down on the earthen floor beyond the foot of Juan's pallet where two lizards were having slippery sex in the mud.

So it was raining still. The cold, driving rain of November which Padre Tómas spoke of in the church: "It is the tears of the Poor Souls in Purgatory which they shed because of the sins of the people of this village."

Juan could hear his mother snoring on her ancient bed in the next room and said a prayer to Saint Jude, patron of hopeless causes, that she would remain asleep until he could get safely away from the house. Not that he really thought that Saint Jude would be disposed to answer such a petition, but he could not face another scene such as he'd had with his mother last night when she discovered that he'd sold the goat for a packet of cigarettes.

It had been a hasty thing to do. They needed money, not cigarettes. But they were American—a pack complete— and Juan felt sure that he could hold out five for himself and still realize as much from the sale of the remaining fifteen as from the scraggly goat whose udder was perpetually dry.

But his mother had not given him a chance to explain. She fell upon him with the broom handle, beating him severely about the head and cursing him for a greedy fool. She tore the cigarettes from his hand, ripped off the top of the package and flung the contents out the window into the rain. Juan rushed out to retrieve them but the beautiful white cylinders were already soaked and disintegrating when he found them so that he had to come back into the house with nothing to show but a few flecks of the excellent tobacco on his fingers. His mother beat him again and sent him off to bed without even half of their one remaining tortilla.

Juan sat up and hurled a sandal at the shameless lizards. Then he lay back again and measured with his hands the dimensions of the great emptiness in his stomach. His mother's snores continued, mounting louder and louder. She is scolding me even yet, he thought, beating me in her sleep, and he tried to shut out the sound.

He would not get up. There was no place to go but out into the rain. He thought of a sunny day in summer when his father was still alive and there had been beans and tacos at almost every meal. There had been a flock of goats then, all fat. Then he thought of the man who had offered him the cigarettes yesterday afternoon.

He had stopped Juan on the road to the village—a huge man, much over six feet in height. He had a wide, thick-featured face with bright red lips, which slid back when he spoke to reveal yellow teeth, long and curving, like tusks. He reminded Juan of the devil who lay writhing under the feet of the statue of San Miguel the Archangel in the church.

"I have a taste for meat tonight," he said. "Sell me your goat."

Juan wondered if a man could truly eat an entire goat at one sitting and decided that this one was capable of it. At the thought of meat, Juan felt his stomach begin to rumble and to still it he rolled over, put his face to the pallet and tried to think of nothing. The rain beat down and the lizards resumed their tireless round. Juan dozed off and almost immediately began to dream.

The rain had stopped and a bright sun poured through his window. Juan dressed and went outside to stretch himself in its warmth. But when he went out through the door it was into shade, not sunshine. The shade was cast by an enormous plant which rose from the exact spot where the cigarettes had fallen. Juan could not see the top of the plant because of the huge, broad leaves which hung on every side, but it must be very tall. Immediately, Juan began to climb the plant, moving easily up the thick stalk. The leaves smelled vaguely of tobacco and it was pleasant moving up and up, now in the sun, now in the shade.

Juan climbed until the house was but a tiny speck below him and still he could see no top to the plant. Up and up he went until he could no longer see the house at all and wisps of gray cloud swept past him. Then, just as he was beginning to tire, he saw a cliff which jutted toward the stalk of the plant from the right and seemed to converge with it a point above him. Quickly he climbed to the place where they met and stepped off onto the ground. He was at the edge of a long, broad meadow which sloped upward toward the horizon. In the distance was a single building with a spire. Juan walked quickly toward it. The building appeared to be a church—white and gleaming, a beautiful structure such as he had never seen. Could this be Heaven, Juan wondered? Had he died of hunger and not even known it?

Juan stopped in front of the church. There was a broad set of steps leading up to a pair of massive bronze doors. Juan climbed the steps and wondered whether it would be better manners to knock or simply push open the doors and step inside as one would usually enter a church. He decided it would be best to knock. But even before his hand could grasp the great metal ring of the knocker, the doors parted and Padre Tómas stood between them, glaring out at him.

"Is it possible," he said in his usual baleful voice, "that

such a one as you presumes to be admitted here?"

There seemed to be another figure standing in the deep shadow just behind Padre Tómas, but Juan could not see who it was.

"Please, Padre," said Juan, "may I not come in for just a moment?"

"What do you think?" Padre Tómas turned and asked the figure in the shadow.

"Under no circumstances. We cannot admit his sort."

Juan started. There was no mistaking his mother's voice. Padre Tómas turned back to Juan, regarding him with an expression of naked distaste.

"You have heard," he said. "Since you may not come in you must go back down. It will not be quite so pleasant as coming up, I assure you." And with that he pushed the doors tightly shut, almost cutting off Juan's nose.

Juan turned and went slowly down the steps. Truly, there seemed nothing to do but go back down and he started slowly out across the meadow toward the distant cliff. The fact that his mother hated him so deeply did not surprise Juan, but he wondered how she came to be inside the strange church. Had she, too, died of hunger? Juan brooded about this as he walked and so did not at first hear the heavy footsteps behind him. When he did, he whirled about in panic and saw that the church doors had been thrown open and already running toward him in full stride came the huge and villainous-looking man to whom he had traded the goat. He was carrying something in his right hand which looked horribly familiar and when he saw that Juan had seen him, began to roar obscenities and threats with every step.

Juan did not wait to see what it was that the man was carrying or what it was he wanted with him but turned immediately and began to run for the stalk. Juan had always considered himself to be a very fine runner, faster than most of the village boys, but now his legs seemed hardly to move and he heard the man's footsteps closing in on him. In his terror, Juan almost ran off the edge of the cliff and only at the last second managed to turn and run along it toward the plant. The man shifted course instantly to cut him off. Only by diving headlong through the air, risking everything, did Juan manage to elude the man's outstretched arm.

To Juan's amazement, the man did not try to follow him down the stalk but instead leaned out above him and watched his incredibly slow and clumsy descent. Then with a great laugh that rolled out and down, beating at Juan's ears like the heavy wings of a bird of prey, the man raised his right arm and hurled the object he'd been carrying.

Juan stopped, paralyzed with fear. The object came toward him slowly, turning lazily in the air, straight for his upturned face. It was the severed head of the goat, the eyes wide open and staring reproachfully at Juan with the mouth split and set in a satanic leer.

In the second before it struck him, Juan saw the man lose his balance and fall from the cliff; heard his roar of fear and outrage. Then Juan himself was falling headlong through the clouds. It grew darker and things brushed against him. The air seemed full of writhing, twisting reptile bodies, intertwined, flailing the air with clawed feet. Juan tried to begin a prayer to his angel guardian but could not think of the words. The man appeared beside him and reached for him even as they fell, his yellow teeth gnashing and shredding the red lips in soundless fury. The ground rushed up to meet them. Juan met it with the top of his head, which split into pieces at the impact.

Juan sat up on the pallet. His mother stood over him holding the broom.

"Get up," she said, "or must I give you another. Padre Tómas has been here with important news. The man to whom you sold the goat has been found dead. A bone caught in his throat and choked him. He was an evil man

—a murderer with a price on his head. Since it was a bone from our goat which killed him, Padre Tómas—what a saintly man he is—persuaded the authorities that the reward should come to me. Your stupidity has brought us a fortune but do not think on that account that I will forgive you."

Juan got up and looked for his sandals. The lizards lay in the corner, dead of exhaustion. Juan dressed and went outside. The sun was not shining but at least it had stopped raining. Juan supposed that he should go to the church, thank Padre Tómas and offer a candle in thanksgiving. Instead, recalling his dream, he decided he would go to have a look at the dead murderer.

Peter Pan

BY *. *. H*TCHN*R

FITSCHEN

I HAD COME A LONG, HARD WAY TO SEE PETER PAN. NEVERLAND, in spite of what you may have read in travel advertisements, is not an easy place to reach and I had not wanted to make the trip in the first place. But my editors—if you can honor such a pack of jackals with the name—insisted. It was my incredibly silly mission to persuade Pan to submit to an interview on the stunning subject "How it feels to be young at ninety-two"—a topic that every magazine in the world must have put before him at least twice a year since he'd turned fifty.

I agreed to come finally only because of my own great desire to meet Peter Pan in the flesh. The odds against this were long, for in recent years he had been seeing fewer and fewer people and virtually no journalists. But even the tenuous prospect of a chance to see with my own eyes the living embodiment of eternal boyhood—the true immortal who had been my one and enduring hero since kindergarten days—was enough to cause me to throw caution and good judgment to the winds. I tried to express this real motive in the letter that I wrote to Pan requesting an appointment, and something of my genuine regard for him must have gotten across, for, amazingly, he agreed to see me.

Still, it was with considerable apprehension that I approached the stately old oak that was the home of Peter Pan. At precisely 10 A.M.—the time specified by Pan in his reply—I tied my card to a small stone and dropped it down the knothole that served as entrance to the famed underground home. Nervous as I was about disturbing a living legend in his sanctuary, I couldn't help but thrill to the moment and the place. So many storied adventures had taken place on the exact spot where I stood that the very air seemed charged with romance. I halfway expected to see Captain Hook come roaring out of the forest in hot pursuit of Wendy and the Lost Boys.

For a while nothing happened. Finally I heard a faint buzzing sound and a second later saw in the dark recess of the knothole a tiny point of intense golden light, which jiggled for a moment in the aperture and then disappeared. Another long minute dragged by and I began to feel uncomfortably certain that I was being made the victim of one of the famous Pan "put-ons." But just as I was about to turn tail and beat a shamefaced retreat I heard the unmistakable sounds of climbing coming from somewhere below my feet, and in another instant there, grinning broadly out of the knothole at me, was the celebrated face of Peter Pan. And the grin was all for me!

With considerable difficulty, since the knothole must have shrunk over the years so that it had become only a fraction of an inch larger than his waist, Pan wriggled head-first out of the tree and stood up. My first impression— which I was rather ashamed to have—was that he was disconcertingly, almost ludicrously, short. The top of his pointed green cap came only to my shoulder and his heavily jowled face was without the faintest trace of a beard. But, if his over-all appearance was something less than heroic, one quickly forgot about it when one noticed his remarkable eyes. They were a cool gray, immensely deep and wise. Tiny amber flecks scuttled about in the depths, mischievously independent and sparklingly defiant. Aside from the bright red feather atop his cap, Pan was dressed completely in green. His doublet was boldly fringed down the sides and sleeves and his legs were covered by skin-hugging tights that seemed stretched to the breaking point where they spanned out to contain his buttocks and undeniably substantial paunch. He was breathing stentoriously from the exertions of the climb and passage through the knothole but he cocked his head to one side, placed his hands on his hips in the classic Peter Pan stance and regarded me with a mock-serious expression of serious scrutiny.

"Tink says on basis her quick recon flight you look like a pirate," he said in a high, piping voice that seemed absurdly slight issuing from a person of his bulk. "You come to pirate me?"

"Mr. Pan," I said, upset that my first words to him had to be so defensive and pedestrian, "I assure you that I'm about the furthest thing imaginable from a pirate."

"Tink probably wrong," he said. "Not for first time, either. Extremely jealous fairy as you may have heard. Allowances must be made."

Pan continued to study me closely. "Nix on 'mister' stuff, though. Even pirates never called me that and they had reason to before it was all over. Friends who count call me Cousin—a handle stuck on by Lost Boys early on in saga. Got to be certified member of Peter Pan Cousin Club to use it, though. You want to join?"

I was tickled right down to the tips of my toes by all this. There was substance to the legends, all right. Peter Pan was all I'd heard and dreamed he was—and more! I hadn't wanted to use the tape recorder at the beginning so I took out my notebook and recorded our conversation thus far before replying, "By all means, if I can measure up."

"Really nothing to it," said Pan. He stretched his short arms, spread them apart and leaned forward onto the balls of his feet. "All you have to do is leap to the top of my tree, like this."

Pan crouched slightly and jumped into the air. Incredibly, he went straight up until he was as high as the top of the oak. There he stopped, defying gravity, and did a somewhat awkward handstand on the highest branch of the tree. He wavered there for almost a minute then did a flip and dropped lightly back to earth beside me.

"I'm afraid that's a rather tall order for me," I said nervously, remembering only too late that Pan reportedly detested puns. "But," I added quickly, "I'll try anything if it means I stand a chance of becoming a certified member of the Peter Pan Cousin Club."

"Positive, 'can-do' attitude is everything," Pan said approvingly. "Just take mind, guts, spine, muscles—all you've got—by scruff of neck and tell them firmly, 'I can fly!' Make it clear to all concerned that you mean serious business and no nonsense need apply. Don't worry too much about handstand at top. Even John and Michael Darling, who were beauty flyers, never managed to get that right."

You can imagine what my feelings were at this point. The prospect of trying to duplicate Pan's stupendous feat quite petrified me. He'd been willing to overlook my unintentional pun but I knew that he'd never forgive me if I backed down on this, did it badly or—Lord forbid!—showed the slightest sign of fear or hesitation. There was nothing to do but try to bluff it through and hope for the best. So, with a quick get-ready signal to the photographer who had accompanied me (and who lay hidden in the bushes behind us), I spread my arms and went up on my feet as Pan had done. If nothing else, the picture might show my editors that I'd been in there pitching.

I closed my eyes and crouched for the hopeless leap. But just as I was ready to launch myself, I felt Pan's chubby hand on my shoulder.

"OK, relax," he said, laughing. "Just wanted to see if you'd try it. You've got what it takes. Welcome to club. Entitles you to all privileges of membership. Want to take a look around grounds?"

"Thanks, Cousin," I said, hugely relieved. "I'd love to."

Pan said we'd need provisions for our tour of Neverland. While he struggled back down inside the tree to get them I checked out my tape recorder and had a brief conference with the photographer. In a few minutes Pan emerged with a huge wicker hamper, which I volunteered to carry. We started out across the island, Pan leading the way.

Our progress was antlike because my remarkable guide stopped every few yards to point out some rock or tree where he'd done battle with pirates, Indians or a wild animal. Pan recalled every smallest detail of each encounter and relived them for me in the most colorful language imaginable. Had it been anyone but Peter Pan I might have grown tired of hearing how he'd managed to come out on top, time after time after time.

After almost an hour of these peripatetic reminiscences we came out of the forest into a clearing. It was about as large as a football field and completely ringed by Indian tepees of the gaudiest colors. Signs were posted everywhere. They advertised everything from soft drinks to souvenirs and small knots of tourists moved through this thicket of commerce, going from one tepee to another, bargaining loudly with the Indians.

The sight seemed to disturb Pan deeply. He put his hand on my arm to indicate that we would not go farther into the clearing.

"Regular three-ring circus," he said, frowning up at me. "Makes me sicker than Hook's poison made Tink. I can hardly recognize the place."

"What happened here, Cousin?" I asked, trying not to stand so tall.

"Nothing except much dramatized and choreographed ambush of Lost Boys by Indians camouflaged as trees. Now Indians would have to disguise themselves as billboards or stick out like sore thumbs."

"Gosh, Cousin!" I said, "Those must have been the days, all right."

But at this moment several tourists spotted us and came charging down on Pan with autograph books at the ready. He grew very pale, turned immediately and went crashing heavily off into the underbrush. I followed as best I could with the ungainly basket. Only when it seemed absolutely certain that no one was following us did Pan finally stop.

"Was extremely close call," he gasped, sitting down on a giant toadstool and indicating that I should put down the basket and do the same.

When he had his breathing back under control, Pan said, "Once a lady tourist equipped with extremely ample bosom cornered me in clearing and demanded that I autograph crumby Indian pot she had just bought for her little boy, Johnny. Was big round pot with large hole in top so I signed it: 'To Johnny, may he go in peace.' Lady tourist was not amused by sentiment and said her image of me had fallen flat on its face. So, there was nothing to do but inscribe pot again: 'To Johnny's mother, who will never fall flat on anything.' "

"That's a riot," I giggled, turning up the tape recorder. "Tell me more, Cousin. What about Wendy, for instance? Was she as pretty and nice as the story made her out to be?"

Pan got a faraway look in his eyes and, for the moment, seemed to forget all about me. Almost mechanically, he reached into the basket and took out a sack of peanut-butter-and-jelly sandwiches, which he ate one after the other in rapid succession, washing them down with great swigs of cold milk from a Thermos. After he'd disposed of perhaps a dozen sandwiches, he peeled a banana for each of us and leaned back, crossing his left leg over his right knee with great difficulty.

"Wendy was pretty all right," he said, "give or take a few warts. But it's necessary to remember that she was nothing but a girl, and an English girl at that. English girls run to talk and pious maxims and are regular demons on personal hygiene. Wendy hadn't been here a week when

Lost Boys and self had been scrubbed to high gloss. And she drove Tink wild, of course. Was extremely glad to get her out of our hair, I assure you."

"Then the ending of the story isn't necessarily as sad as everyone usually takes it to be?" I asked, declining the piece of fudge cake that Pan offered me.

"I'll level with you," said Pan, narrowing his eyes, "that girl really messed up my life. Besides health and hygiene kick, she fixed it so I had no out but to kill poor old Hook —who was senile, anyway—and chase off pirates. Things have been dull as hell around here ever since. Nobody to fight. Nobody to sneak up on. You saw for yourself what the Indians have become. It's enough to make me want to grow up."

Pan looked thoroughly miserable but before I could think of anything properly sympathetic to say, he sat up straight and seemed to will himself out of the doldrums.

"To answer your question properly," he said crisply, "ending was best part of story and happened just in nick of time as Wendy was about one month from puberty when she got home. Went back to see her a few years later and she was already hopelessly filled out and married to a jerk solicitor. Very disgusting. Husband patted me on head and called me 'Dear Peter!' while Wendy talked continuous stream of crap about wanting all her boys to grow up to look just like me."

Pan stood up and stretched. "Was valuable lesson," he said. "Accurate picture of what would have happened to me if Wendy stayed in Neverland—life with soap-crazed mother."

All this was perfectly fascinating to me, of course, as I was sure it would be to my editors. A little more on the old tape and I'd be able to retire. But Pan suddenly seemed anxious to get going so I picked up the basket and prepared to follow. I decided to risk one more question before we started.

"And Tiger Lily?" I said. "She was always a great

favorite of mine. Whatever happened to her after you rescued her from the tide?"

Pan looked at me with just the faintest trace of exasperation in his eyes. He sighed, took a candy bar out of the basket and sat down again.

"Contrary to all published reports," he said between bites, "Tiger Lily was not a princess. Not even an Indian, for that matter."

This was real news and I let my face go all agog. "Holy cow, Cousin!"

"Never told anyone this before," continued Pan, "and probably shouldn't now, but T. L. was illegitimate daughter of Mother Goose and Robin Hood. Have always felt partly responsible because they met through me. Had known both parties for a long time and issued standing invitations to visit tree whenever they could. Never dreamed both would show up on same weekend."

Pan wadded the candy wrapper into a ball and swallowed it. "Miss Goose was real looker in those days but was running out of nursery rhymes and beginning to hit the bottle. Hood was never as noble as stories made him out. Was really an outlaw who lost his nerve. Only reason he quit robbing poor was that it didn't pay. At that time he had forest fever of worst sort from hiding out so long in Sherwood Forest with so-called merry men and only an occasional note from Maid Marian to cheer him up.

"No need to spell it out. Tink and I knew we had our work as chaperones cut out right from the beginning and fixed it to keep an eye on them around the clock in shifts. But on Saturday night we got called out on a false alarm— one of Hook's specialties before he went dotty—and that's when the milk got spilled. Anyway, about a year later Miss Goose comes back with a baby girl and asks me what she should do as her reputation with the kids is just not going to stand up if the word gets out and nobody seemed willing to go to Sherwood and serve a paternity summons on Hood. The poor kid was just about to crack and drinking worse than ever so I fixed it with the Indians to take the baby and raise her like a princess. Worked out just fine as T. L. had dark complexion and turned out to be one hell of a fine shot with the bow and arrow."

"Gee, Cousin," I said, stunned, "is that why we call Miss Goose 'Mother' now, in spite of nobody knowing why?"

"That's the true gen," Pan replied, getting up again. "And as long as you've got your thumb in the record book, have you ever wondered where the expression 'wild goose chase' came from?"

"You don't mean it," I gasped.

Pan looked up at me sheepishly and said, "I don't like to stop the horses when they are running so well and don't want you to get wrong notion about my general state of vim and vigor, but even when you're perpetually young a morning like this can grind you down. We'll finish tour another time but right now had better make tracks back to the old tree for afternoon pills and siesta."

I've never been one to crowd my luck or to take advantage of another's good nature, so I agreed at once that we should return. Slowly Pan led the way back through the clearing where the Indians were setting up bleachers for a commemorative pageant of the ambush. By the time we reached the tree Pan was scarcely able to put one foot in front of the other and I realized that it was only out of deference to me that he had walked back at all instead of flying.

"He's really quite a fellow," I said softly into the tape recorder, thinking as I did that the television people might well be interested in the results of our little junket. I just hoped that the photographer had kept his movie camera going.

As if in answer to my whispered comment, I heard a buzzing from the tree and saw a brief, solicitous flash of light in the knothole. Pan noticed it, too, for he turned abruptly and took my right hand in both of his.

"Tink probably blames you for keeping me out so long,"

he said, "but have enjoyed every minute of it and will clear you with her. Tink makes mistakes about people but I seldom do."

He gave my hand a final squeeze, seized the picnic basket and tossed it down through the knothole. Then, grunting with exertion, he joined his hands together above his head like a diver and plunged headlong after the basket. It was a magnificent piece of bravado and a well-aimed dive, but unfortunately, what had come out of the hole before lunch now refused resolutely to return and Pan stuck solidly at the waist. His arms and legs suddenly appeared to grow directly from the trunk of the tree.

"Damn sandwiches!" I heard his muffled shout. "Push me through!" At the same time the grotesquely disembodied legs began to flail the air wildly and the already badly overextended tights gave up the unequal struggle and burst asunder.

The photographer broke cover and came running up, snapping a series of color close-ups as fast as he could work his camera.

"What's the matter with you!" I shouted. "Haven't you any respect at all? I'll give you just two more rolls to stop that!"

For, ludicrous as the sight might have seemed to some, it really tore me up to see brave old Pan caught in such a painful and embarrassing fix (again, no pun intended). I was just thinking seriously of cabling my editors for advice when the buzzing started up again, much louder than before, and Pan suddenly—almost miraculously—slipped from view.

Tink to the rescue once again, I thought, picking up Pan's ravished tights from where they had fallen outside the hole. What a marvelous souvenir they made, or with a little altering and mending, they might look pretty good on me.

The photographer was beside himself with joy. "What a

tremendous spread that last sequence is going to make," he chortled. "I've captured the very essence of 'How it feels to be young at ninety-two.' "

"Come on!" I said, not bothering to hide the disgust I felt for the brute. "If we hurry, we've just got time to catch the Indians' matinee at the clearing."

Beowulf

BY M*LC*LM M*GG*R*DG*

SINCE DEALING WITH THE BIBLE IN THESE PAGES TWO YEARS ago, I really can't recall approaching a book with more distaste than I feel for this one. As was the case with that unwieldy and impossible tome, *Beowulf* comes to us *sans* author. Now one can well understand the author's desire not to have his name associated with such claptrap, but it is exasperating in the extreme to be forced to play the juvenile game of Riddly-Riddly-Ree in consequence of this late-blooming prudence.

Forced, I say, because any critic who does not hasten to post a conspicuous public guess as to the identity of the perpetrator of these anonymous botches is himself very apt to be taxed with being the author. Or else the ensuing orgy of speculation impels knowledgeable persons with weak stomachs to step forward and set the record straight, if only because they shall retch if exposed to one further paragraph of asinine conjecture.

My celebrated review of the Bible is an excellent case in point. I had utterly no intention of noticing the book when it first appeared and disposed of my advance reading copy with sanitary gloves and tongs immediately upon having glanced through it. But some baboon came out in *The Times* with an article setting forth all the clues that caused his handicapped brain to conclude that the Bible had actually been written by God. I knew this to be patent rot, of course, and had no alternative but to reveal that when last we'd lunched together, God denied categorically having had anything whatsoever to do with the book.

And now we seem to be in the midst of a similarly absurd flap as to the paternity of *Beowulf*. One can read of nothing else. In the past three days alone I've seen it seriously put forward that the book is the work of (1) Princess Margaret Rose, because of the overdone party scenes in Heorot, the great hall, where so much of the story takes place; (2) the Rolling Stones, because they so faithfully mirror the physical description of the monster, Grendel; and (3) Adolf Hitler (who, according to this extremely well-informed advocate, not only still lives, but positively thrives in a plush hideaway beneath the Vatican), because of certain stylistic resemblances to *Mein Kampf* and the book's strident celebration of Nordic supremacy.

You will see, then, why it is imperative that I enter the lists once again, even at this late date. Thanks to Tony Richardson's film version, which everyone has seen, I am at least spared the onerous task of recounting *Beowulf's* moribund plot. In passing, however, I do want to doff my cap to the film's producer for the inspiration that gave us the stalwart Peter O'Toole as Beowulf, whose grip was reputed to equal that of thirty strong men. Less inspired, I felt, was the choice of Terry Thomas for the role of King Hrogthar, or of Julie Christie for the key part of Grendel's mother. Mr. Thomas' physique does not show to good advantage in caribou fur, and stunning as she was in the underwater battle scenes, Miss Christie somehow is simply not convincing as anybody's mother, much less Sir Laurence Olivier's. Larry, however, made a quite satisfactory Grendel and, no doubt, a most economical one since he apparently was able to employ the same get-up he used for *Othello*.

There has never been any question in my mind concerning the identity of the author of *Beowulf*. His name is stamped on the book's every page. In fact, it's so obvious that one wonders anew at the bottomless stupidity of our so-called literary establishment. For their cretinous benefit, then, I make the weary trip to the chalkboard, pointer in hand. Tap! Tap! You there in the back with your fingers plugging the vacuum between your ears—attention!

Since *Beowulf* can't possibly be taken seriously it must, in consequence, be an allegory. Since it is an allegory it must certainly be political. Since it is political allegory it must, in this unlettered age, be topical.

Once this is grasped it is simply a matter of matching things up: the monster, Grendel, is De Gaulle to the teeth, backed up his voracious mother, the Common Market; Hrogthar is surely the Prime Minister, just as Heorot is England; Beowulf himself, with his bad manners, vulgar boasting and propensity for crossing water uninvited, amounts practically to a map of the United States. And so, drearily, forth.

You will pardon my yawn then, I'm sure, as I point out that there is only one mind whose general disorder and lack of restraint could spawn such an epic of transparency. Ah! I see a glimmer of intelligence trying vainly to gain a foothold on a few narrow foreheads. Of course, it just has to be!

Let there be an end to all and sundry speculation. I give it to you here and now and forever, for mine is the kingdom and the power and the glory, that the author of *Beowulf* is none other than that consummately ubiquitous, that artful nondodger, that purveyor of middle to brow —C. P. Snow.

Winnie the Pooh

BY FL*NN*R* *'C*NN*R

FITSCHEN

AT SUNDOWN THE BOY, RUFUS, WHO WAS EIGHT, CAME OUT
on the porch and sat down on the top step in front of
where his grandmother was rocking.

"You come down off Pout Mountain yet?" asked the
grandmother. Earlier in the day Rufus's stepmother, Winifred, had caught him smoking a catalpa pod behind the
chicken house and beat him with a barrel stave. Rufus hid
himself under the house and sulked there, not even coming out for supper.

"She shouldn't oughta have hit me like that," Rufus pro-
tested. "If Pap were still alive he'd kick her teeth in for me.
Why'd he have to take up with her anyhow? Nothin' but
Birmingham trash."

"Don't let it take you so hard," said the grandmother,
who had asked the same question of herself. "Suppose I
tell you a story before we go to bed? It might ease your
spirit."

"It won't ease my spirit none if it's about any of them
talkin' animals which is really a fairy prince that's been
bushwhacked by some witch. You must have told me a
hundert of them. Don't you know any stories where somebody ends up trompin' their stepmother in the face?"

"No," said the grandmother, "but I do know a story
about a boy and a bear."

"What was the boy's name," Rufus asked, intrigued in
spite of himself.

"His name was C. R. and he was about your age or a
little younger and he lived in a cabin in the piney woods
just about like this one."

117

"What was C. R. the short of?" asked Rufus.

"Christopher Robin," said the grandmother.

"I can see why he wanted people to call him C. R., all right," said Rufus. "What happened about the bear?"

"If you'll keep shut for a spell, I'll tell you," said the grandmother. "It begins when C. R. was out in the woods one day, hunting squirrels with a .22, when he comes across this bear sittin' alongside a cyprus stump. It wasn't a big bear so C. R. figured he'd just have a shot at him from a far piece and take off runnin' in case he missed a mortal wound."

"What color was the bear?" Rufus demanded.

"What difference does that make?" the grandmother replied. "I thought you wanted this story to move along."

"Everything makes a difference," said Rufus. "I got to know what color was the bear."

"Well," said the grandmother, looking hard at the back of Rufus's scrawny neck where the top end of a welt still showed, "it wasn't black nor brown nor any of your regular bear colors. I'd say it was a kind of a washed-out carrot color, about the shade of your stepmother's hair."

"Good," said Rufus, "now tell me about how he shot it in the gut."

"Hold on there, Mister," said the grandmother. "This is my story and I'll say what happened next if it's all the same to you. As a matter of fact, Rufus didn't fire on the bear at all, on account of when he was just fixin' to pull the trigger the bear ups and says, 'Don't shoot!' "

"I knew it," said Rufus. "A talkin' bear. I'll bet he was really a fairy prince all along. You only got one string on your banjo, like I said."

"You're just like your pap when he was a boy," said the grandmother. "Full of sass and vinegar. Think you know how many beans is in the bag afore you count them." She gave Rufus a sharp poke in the ribs with her cane.

"The bear could talk all right, because this here was a

'chanted forest," she continued, "but it weren't no fairy prince. It told C. R. its name was Pooh, and that if he didn't shoot, it'd show him where lots of varmits lived that he could shoot."

"Pooh?" said Rufus. "That ain't no kind of name for a bear. You can't even tell if it's a him or a her."

"That's right, you can't," said the grandmother, who went right on with the story. "C. R. figured he might as well go along with the bear as he could shoot it any time he wanted and still get a pack of other game as well.

"First off, the bear takes him to a hole in the side of a hill. 'Come out here for a minute, Rabbit!' yells the bear. And sure enough a rabbit pokes his head out long enough for C. R. to blast him.

" 'That's one,' says the bear and leads C. R. off to a clearing where this funny little wild donkey and a baby pig is walkin' round in a circle together like they was talkin' over something mighty serious. C. R. kneels down and gets them both, neat as you please. 'That's two and three,' says the bear."

"You really 'spect me to swallow that?" said Rufus, spitting to show what he thought of the story so far.

The grandmother raised her cane again.

"Go ahead," Rufus said, "I ain't sick to my stomach yet."

"Next the bear takes C. R. to a big tree with a rope hanging down out of it. 'When I pull this here rope you be ready to shoot,' says the bear. He yanks on the rope and right away an owl comes out of a knothole and sits there on a limb blinkin' and turnin' his head till C. R. lines one up into his gizzard.

" 'That's four and a good shot, I don't mind tellin' you,' says the bear."

"Anybody that can't knock a hoot-owl out of a tree ought to have his gun took away," Rufus said under his breath.

"Just then C. R. hears a terrible roar and turns round to see a tiger bearin' down on him like the morning freight. 'You're on your own,' says the bear, duckin' behind the tree.

"Now C. R. weren't countin' on running into no tigers and it gave him a mean start. But he wasn't no boy to lose his head so he throws up the .22 and shoots."

"Ain't no .22 made gonna stop no tiger," said Rufus, disgusted.

"Boy," said the grandmother, "what you don't know could fill a silo. That bullet went smack down the tiger's throat and busted his spleen. Ever'body who's been to a Tar Sam movie in Birmingham knows that's the only place to jab a tiger. He was dead afore he hit the ground."

"It was a mighty lucky shot then," said Rufus, more impressed than he cared to admit.

"That's just what the bear said when he came out from behind the tree," the grandmother went on. " 'Five must be your lucky number,' he told C. R. and led him off into the woods again, farther than C. R.'d ever been before, to where there was a little house."

"Who lived there?" asked Rufus, forgetting himself.

"You got the patience of a bitch in heat, ain't you?" said the grandmother. "Only they got better manners." She was pleased, all the same, that Rufus took such an interest in her story.

"It turned out it was the bear's house. It bein' able to talk and all you don't s'pose it'd be livin' in some cave, did you?"

"A course not," said Rufus.

"And hoppin' around in front of the house was two of the strangest lookin' critters that C. R. had ever seen—a big un and a little un—with long tails and terrible big bottom feet. They looked like giant rats, only they sat up on their hind legs and covered about a rod ever'time they took a jump.

" 'Them is kangaroos,' the bear told C. R., 'and you better shoot 'em fast else they'll kick the bejesus out of you.' Well, C. R. he didn't like their looks much so he gets the big one first and then the little one—right in the middle of a hop.

" 'That's six and seven,' says the bear . . ."

"What's all this fool countin' for," Rufus interrupted again. "Sounds to me like you just can't think a nothin' else for the bear to say."

"It's a good thing for you that you don't have no school to go to," said the grandmother triumphantly, "cause they'd throw you back the first day for not bein' able to see the book in front of your nose. How many shots does that old .22 of your pap's hold?"

"Seven," said Rufus, realizing that he'd let his grandmother lead him into a trap.

"That's right," she said. "And so did C. R.'s. And that bear, Pooh, who was smarter'n you and C. R. put together, he knew it too.

" 'Now you've cut it, boy,' says the bear to C. R. 'You're clean out of bullets and I'm goin' to have you for lunch. I'm obliged to you for shootin' all them other pests for me and also for comin' right along to my house so nice like. I hates to drag my food a long way.' And with that he jumps at C. R. and tries to get a hold on his throat."

Rufus could stand it no longer. "You goin' to let that runty carrot-colored bear get the best of him?" he shouted. "It's a mighty poor kind of story if you do."

"Got you worried, ain't I?" cackled the grandmother. "As it happened, old C. R. was just a might too fast for the bear. He just took a little step to the side and let the bear sail by him and fall flat on its face. Then C. R. takes the rifle by the barrel and beats the bear over the head with the butt till it was stone cold dead."

"That's more like it," said Rufus, pleased. "That's the best story you've ever told."

The grandmother was just about to ask Rufus if he felt like eating a bite of supper now when she was brought up short by a shout from inside the cabin.

"Can't you two stop that eternal caterwaulin' out there?" It was Rufus's stepmother calling from her bed. "My head's like to split it aches so bad and I don't aim to stand for all that racket. This here is my house now and don't neither of you forget it!"

"Don't you fret yourself none, Winifred," the grandmother called back, "Rufus and me was just fixin' to go to bed."

To Rufus, in a much lower tone of voice she said, "Fancy that, she's got a headache now. Ain't that a pity?"

"That's eight," said Rufus, smiling for the first time all day.